EXPLORING THE DEEP

Other titles by the same author

Operation Spetsnaz
Combat Frogmen
Frogman Spy
Naval Elite
Successful Holidays
Maritime Elite

Patrick Stephens Limited, an imprint of Haynes Publishing, has published authoritative, quality books for enthusiasts for more than 25 years. During that time the company has established a reputation as one of the world's leading publishers of books on aviation, maritime, military, model-making, motor cycling, motoring, motor racing, railway and railway modelling subjects. Readers or authors with suggestions for books they would like to see published are invited to write to The Editorial Director, Patrick Stephens Limited, Sparkford, Nr. Yeovil, Somerset BA22 7JJ.

EXPLORING THE DEEP

The quest to conquer earth's last frontier

Michael Welham

Patrick Stephens Limited

First published in 1994

British Library Cataloguing-in-Publication Data: A catalogue record for this book is available from the British Library

ISBN 1 85260 471 9

Library of Congress catalog card number 94 77772

Patrick Stephens Limited is an imprint of Haynes Publishing, Sparkford, Nr. Yeovil, Somerset BA22 7JJ.

Typeset by G&M, Raunds, Northamptonshire
Printed in Great Britain by Butler & Tanner Ltd, London and Frome

Contents

Author's Note

I HAVE BEEN involved with matters underwater for most of my life, and so writing this book has been both a challenge and of great personal interest. Since the late 1960s the world of the oceanographer and professional diver has changed dramatically, with technology making the most impact, particularly with the development of specialist surface support vessels and underwater vehicles.

I have endeavoured to produce a book that is as diverse as the subject itself, and as such have recorded some of the more notable achievements and developments of human exploration and work below the surface of the world's oceans and seas. Interest in the subject was originally sparked by a series of articles that I wrote for the magazine *Scuba World*.

This book is neither a complete detailed history nor a technical manual, but a combination of information, drawings and photographs that will provide an insight for the uninitiated into the fascination, technology and dangers involved with the exploration of the deep, the earth's last frontier.

* * *

I would like to thank those companies and individuals whose assistance has been invaluable in the preparation of this book. Special thanks must go to those organizations outside the UK who provided information and photographs to show the international flavour of undersea research, exploration and development. Though the list below is not in any order, I have endeavoured to include everybody concerned, but if I have omitted a name then please accept my thanks and apologies. In particular I owe a debt of gratitude to Jacqui Welham, who has provided valuable support and endured the implications of a tight deadline. Lastly, thanks to the publisher, who has supported the book from inception to completion.

Special thanks go to: Julie Welham, whose interpretation and word-processing skills transformed my hand-written scribble into a readable manuscript. Without her support this book would never have been written; David Bray FNI, a Senior Lecturer at Lowestoft College, for his valuable input on Dynamic Positioning; Michele Fructus of Comex S.A., France; The Woods Hole Oceanographic Institution, USA; The US Naval Oceanographic Office and the Departments of the US Navy for their valuable contributions of information and photographs; Mr H. Talkington of the Development, Test & Evaluation Naval Command Control & Oceans Surveillance Department, US Navy; Vanessa Alexander and Mike O'Meara of Rockwater Ltd; The Marine Information and Advisory Service of the Institute of Oceanographic Sciences; Texas A & M University, USA; Dragerwerk AG, Germany; Van Oord ACZ, Netherlands; Bruker Meerestechnik GmBH, Germany; The National Hyperbaric Centre, Aberdeen, Scotland; Oceaneering International; Soil Machine Dynamics; Atlantis Submarines, Canada; Perry Tritech, USA; International Hard Suits, Canada; Oilfield Publications Ltd; Jane's Data Division; B.T. Marine; Prodive Ltd; Cable and Wireless (Marine) Ltd; Northern Ocean Services Ltd; Shell U.K.;

Statoil, Norway; and Amerada Hess.

My thanks are also extended to the following individuals for their contributions: Frank Murray, Arnold Huddy, Gordon Clark, B. J. Walzak and Victor Humphrey.

Those pictures which have not been credited to anyone else are my own, apart from one or two where it was not possible to trace the copyright.

Michael G. Welham

Introduction

WITH SOME 70 per cent of the Earth's surface consisting of water, virtually all of it remains unexplored, creating an aura of mystery and a touch of adventure about those who dare to penetrate beneath the water's surface. Interest is such that in recent years a growing band of amateur explorers have become scuba divers and entered the alien world. It offers its own special rewards, but they are restricted in the main to shallow water and locations where boats and diving equipment are available.

Even for those who touch the edge of the mysteries of the oceans, there remains a longing to know more of what is hidden and unseen. In fact, we know more about the moon's surface than we do about the ocean floor. Major film productions such as *The Abyss* have added to the mystery by portraying a free-swimming diver who breathes liquid oxygen and can descend to a depth of 5 km (3 miles).

Human beings are not equipped to live underwater without special equipment because they only have the ability to hold their breath for a few minutes, and body heat rapidly diminishes when immersed in water, especially cold water. The effect can be fatal in a short period of time. Even the human eye creates a blurred image when underwater and hearing is much reduced with a very limited ability to determine direction. It can be argued that modern diving equipment counters many of these problems, and that with thermal body covering, a suitable breathing system and an underwater refuge, humans could adapt to living underwater. However, there is no fresh air and virtually no light – two elements that the human body requires while living on dry land.

The French underwater explorer Jacques Cousteau is convinced that human beings could live underwater without using their lungs, and that they would only need rubber fins and webbed gloves to aid movement underwater. Underwater people would have their lungs sealed off, having been filled with a special liquid to prevent them from being compressed when subjected to external pressure. Breathing would be achieved by a chemical device surgically implanted into the body which would oxygenate the blood. In an experiment in the USA, an individual's lungs were filled with a liquid, enabling them to breathe underwater. The experiment lasted for some 45 minutes, and was considered successful.

Professor J. Kylstra of Duke Medical Centre, North Carolina, USA, found

The multi-functional service vessel Stadive *in dry dock undergoing a refit. The vessel is designed to serve as an emergency fire fighting and support ship for routine diving and maintenance operations in the North Sea. The* Stadive *has a two-bell diving system and is able to support 24 divers in saturation at one time. Part of the diving system includes a Perry Oceanographics PC1805 submarine, which can operate with a pilot and co-pilot to a depth of 200 m (656 ft). (Shell UK Exploration and Production)*

On the Ocean Drilling Programme's drill ship, the JOIDES Resolution, drilling continues 24 hours a day and the activity takes place on the drill floor where the drill crew makes up stands of drill pipe. Each stand of pipe is made up of three lengths of pipe, each 9.5 m (31 ft) long. Here the crew align two drill stands for joining. They will use a device called an iron roughneck to spin the stands of pipe together. When drilling to maximum depth, the drill crew will have to run some 9,144 m (30,000 ft) of pipe. (Texas A&M University)

through experiments on animals that an artificial gill can be inserted into the body with only minor surgery. This would allow the blood to pass through a membrane of silicone rubber external to the body, to be oxygenated by a gas exchange with water outside. These ideas and research projects are not new, though their viability to date can be judged from the fact that development and research have concentrated on conventional diving equipment, systems and underwater vehicles, and this book too will principally tell the story of developments in these more conventional fields. However, that is not to say that further attempts to place humans underwater with a means of maintaining life will not be made with increasing vigour in the foreseeable future.

The major steps forward in design, development and operations have come about through the work of brilliant and adventurous engineers and divers over hundreds of years. All have had the same aim: to put man and machine deeper into the oceans.

The early pioneers discovered that though it was possible to put a man, in

diving equipment, under the water to greater and greater depths, it was another matter to bring him back to the surface without subjecting him to the 'bends' (decompression sickness) or even causing his death. Eventually this led to the introduction and continued development of diving bells and decompression chambers, and the transfer between the two, combined with the development of diving tables that required the use of animals (goats in particular) as well as human volunteers. The experiments with diving tables, decompression chambers and breathing gases have continued throughout the years, from the early pioneers to the divers of today, some of whom have descended to depths of 686 m (2,250 ft) under experimental conditions.

In addition to conventional diving methods, submersible vehicles evolved that would carry scientists, engineers and military personnel to new frontiers. The Americans led the way initially, with the research and development of underwater vehicles for military purposes, but this was closely followed by the development of vehicles for deep ocean research. It was the need of the oil and gas industry in the North Sea for underwater expertise that created a surge of interest in the research and development of underwater vehicles.

Teams of scientists wanted to remain underwater, in saturation conditions, for extended periods. This required the use of underwater habitats that provided living and working facilities as well as making it possible for the team to work away from the habitat using conventional diving equipment. The habitat had to be connected to the surface throughout an operation and therefore had to remain in a fixed location. This suited some projects, but others, in particular those in the oil and gas industry, sought a more flexible system.

The answer lay in the development of small submarines that could be launched from the stern of a mother ship, carry divers to the work site and allow them to 'lock out' and undertake their specific tasks. This had been done with small submerged submarines during the Second World War, but not to depths of 91.5–183 m (300–600 ft), nor for submerged time periods in excess of eight hours. A variety of small submarines were constructed, many of which were not able to deploy divers. They carried observers to deep and remote parts of the oceans to carry out a wide range of operations both in the off-shore oil and gas industry and detailed and specific scientific studies. These small submersibles had to be deployed from surface support vessels, and as a consequence were costly to operate. This all added to the expense and complexities involved in putting man underwater; however, that just offered another challenge to the engineers, designers and developers to find more cost-effective systems.

It was possible to encase a man in a steel suit, where he was not subjected to external water pressure, and deploy him to depths beyond those that could be reached by a conventional diver. Years of research had gone into creating such a suit that would overcome the problems of the external water pressure that reacted on the joints, making them difficult to move. It was not until 1968 that a viable production model was produced and tested, with special joints that enabled it to work at the deeper depths. Once the basic concept was established, other suits, known as Atmospheric Diving Suits because the man inside remained at atmospheric pressure, entered the scene. Each has something different to offer, but the new 'Newt' Suit has taken underwater engineering ingenuity to new limits.

It was evident that there were numerous problems connected with putting a man underwater, especially in deeper water, apart from the obvious ones of cost and risk. Therefore the next step to be considered was to devise a system that could put the tools that divers and the small submarines used into the water, and control them from the surface. This resulted in some of the most prolific research and development that has occurred with underwater systems, and produced Remote Operated Vehicles (ROVs). The smallest are called eyeballs, because of the vast array of electronics involved. The idea behind a remote operated vehicle is to put a machine in the water to replace a

diver. That of course will not happen in the foreseeable future, but underwater machines are readily available, in a variety of sizes and abilities, and are here to stay. Control of the vehicle when it is under the water is undertaken from a control unit located on the structure or vessel. A pilot 'flies' the vehicle in much the same way as a helicopter pilot flies his aircraft, the difference being that while one pilot has a feel for the machine's movements in the air, the other is remote and relies on a tele-

A diver uses a Seaprobe P200 digital readout gauge to measure the wall thickness of legs and bracings. (Gordon Clark)

Divers use a variety of underwater tools and measuring devices to undertake detailed inspections of underwater steel structures.

The Deep Drone *ROV, which provides a deep search and recovery vehicle for the US Navy, is launched on its umbilical by a crane. The vehicle was used during the salvage operations for the downed Korean airliner.* (US Navy)

vision monitor. Power, television and command cables are provided in the form of an umbilical, which links the control unit to the vehicle. Developments with ROVs have led to a variety of models, from the smallest unit, which can be carried in a suitcase, to the large, powerful work systems fitted with a variety of manipulators and tools which can undertake all manner of work and scientific projects.

The exploration of the deep ocean requires both manned and unmanned vehicles depending upon the task that has to be undertaken. Manned vehicles are used to transport scientists and their research equipment to the deepest part of the ocean for specific projects. A problem arose with the need to survey large expanses of seabed. Manned vehicles are costly to construct and operate as well as having limited underwater operating time periods, and they are very weather-dependent. They also require a large, stable and reliable surface support vessel. An ROV also requires a surface support vessel, and while this may be smaller it needs to be able to remain in one position or track and follow the vehicle when it is in the water, because the ROV is linked to the surface through its umbilical and tether.

The answer to this problem came with the development of a new breed of underwater vehicles in the form of robots. They can operate by using pre-programmed

computers carried within the vehicle, while others have computers on board that are programmed by water acoustic signals from a surface support vessel. In either case, it means that there are no physical links to the surface, and that leaves the vehicle independent. This offers a major advantage in that large areas of the seabed can be surveyed, and objects located and identified.

While one group of scientists wants to know how the seabed is formed, and what life-forms reside on and around it, there are those who want to explore beyond, and that means drilling holes into the seabed, in the deepest parts of the ocean, in order to recover samples of the Earth's crust. This work requires a specialist drilling vessel that can remain at sea in one position, drill a hole in the deep ocean and extract samples. These samples provide scientists and technicians with valuable information that can be studied offshore in the vessel's laboratory facilities. Samples are also sent to various institutes throughout the world, where further and more detailed studies are undertaken, and new exploration sites can be identified.

Deep ocean studies that have evoked considerable interest are those involving some of the planet's most beautiful and intelligent creatures. There are well-organized research programmes, undertaken by bona fide institutions, in which dolphins, whales and sea-lions have been trained to aid man in his exploration of the oceans. It has been discovered that these animals can search for and locate items of equipment, and be fitted with special tools to recover them. They have also been trained to work with divers, fetching tools for them and learning to locate and rescue lost divers. While some mammals are part of training programmes, others, held in captivity or in the wild, are observed as part of ongoing research programmes, to study their behaviour and communications. All of these programmes have helped to extend man's knowledge and understanding of the oceans and the wildlife that lives there. As a result of increased interest, individuals can now travel in small groups to various parts of the world to study these creatures in the wild. The undersea world is also being explored by more people with the increasing number of tourist submarines that are being sited in the more exotic locations. They carry passengers in comfort and safety around the undersea world of reefs and wrecks, to view the splendour and observe a considerable variety of marine life.

With man exploring the oceans, its marine life, the seabed and beyond, the growing number of structures, cables and pipelines on the seabed need to be safeguarded from damage and, in the case of pipelines, reduce the risk of pollution. How do you bury or protect a cable or pipeline when it is laid on the seabed? Again the challenge has been met and there are now seabed tractors, towed ploughs or the controlled and accurate placing of large quantities of stone on the seabed, all of which can be done in either deep or shallow water. Every one of these systems is in regular use in the world's seas and oceans, and draws yet again upon man's ingenuity in identifying and solving problems in an alien environment.

When the North Sea oil platform *Piper Alpha* was engulfed in a fireball, divers were at work underwater inspecting the platform's legs and supports. As debris fell around them, they came to the surface and with the support team made good their escape. It is a fact that without divers, and the vital work that they have undertaken, oil and gas would not have been extracted from beneath the North Sea. Yet this is only part of the story, for there are many others behind the scenes who have had major input into the development of sub-sea machine equipment. As the search for oil moved into deeper water, divers and all manner of underwater vehicles had to follow, combating not only the challenge of water depths but the hostile environment. That required the development of saturation diving complexes that can hold up to 16 men, encased in steel tanks, pressurized to a depth equal to that of the water depth. The divers are then confined for weeks at a time breathing a strange gas mixture that makes them speak like Donald Duck.

They have to rely on those outside the chamber for their very existence.

Saturation diving systems and submersible vehicles needed large specialist vessels that could offer more flexibility on operations and remain in position without anchors. That required a vessel using a computer-based system called Dynamic Positioning (DP). The vessel has to be able to set up at location quickly and remain in that one place, often with no objects on the surface to relate to, for periods of days

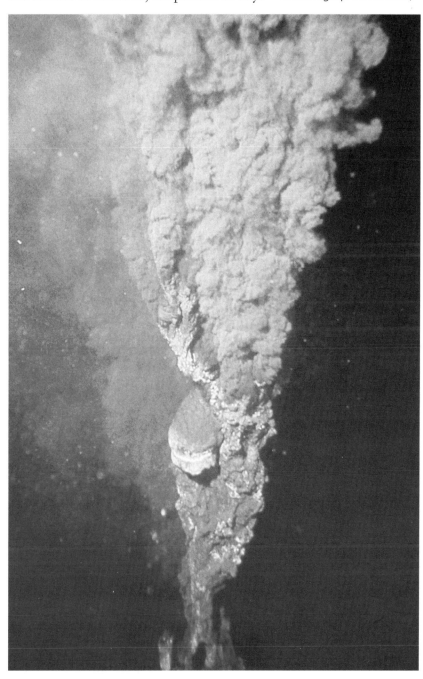

'Black Smoker' hydrothermal vents located in the deep oceans, release warm water from beneath the sea bed. (Woods Hole Oceanographic Institute)

The Jason Junior *remote operated vehicle explores the bow of the* Titanic. (Woods Hole Oceanographic Institute)

tonnes can remain in position, even when close alongside a platform, for unlimited periods. In recent years DP has progressed to be installed on a wide range of vessels, including large offshore drilling platforms and oil tankers.

Underwater technology is readily accepted by those who work with it, but those who are not familiar with the developments and operations may find it difficult to understand the barriers and problems that have and still do face all of those involved in underwater exploration, research and technological developments. This book aims to tell the story of man's struggle to unlock the mysteries of the deep and to work in such an alien environment. This has always been a challenge, for unlike space travel, where the visual image is readily accepted, images from the seabed or deep oceans are often less inspiring, and even though we accept the seas and oceans, the sky can be seen, whereas the deep ocean seabed cannot. The early pioneers met the challenge enthusiastically, with methods that were often dangerous and eccentric, but many of the lessons learned by them still hold good today, enabling us to take our undersea exploration on to new and greater limits of endeavour.

or weeks. This has to be achieved so that the vessel can rotate to move its heading, to keep its bow into the prevailing weather, all without the use of anchors. Technology has developed a computer system that uses surface, satellite and sub-sea reference systems to link into the vessel's 'auto pilot', which controls the propulsion units in a push and pull action to hold the vessel on location. Which means that a Diving Support Vessel of some 9,000

Chapter 1

The Early Days

THE EARTH'S GREAT oceans and seas cover seven-tenths of the globe, with the Pacific Ocean alone covering an area of 163 million sq km (63 million sq miles). The sea is deeper than the land is high, for the average depth of the seabed is about 3,657 m (12,000 ft) compared to an average height on land of only 762 m (2,500 ft).

The oceans are not composed of uniform masses of water but are made up of a series of layers, each differing in temperature and salt content, and each supporting its own form of marine life.

The seabed itself is not the same as the land but is composed of a thin layer of sediment overlying heavy basaltic rocks. This means that for the most part, the oceans and seas have rather uninteresting landscapes. Explorers of the underwater world portray reefs with their myriad of interesting marine life such as whales, sharks and dolphins, and the dramatic exploration of deep sea shipwrecks such as the *Titanic*. Exploring the world's oceans and seas is considered to be an adventure into the last of the Earth's great frontiers, and as a result, there is a developing technical history which enables divers, scientists and engineers to descend to deeper depths and for longer periods.

The world's history is full of the exploits of astronomers who studied the skies and dreamed of space travel. Throughout those times there were also intrepid explorers who were already at work exploring the shallow regions of the world's oceans. Human exploration of the sea involving free-swimming divers with no underwater breathing apparatus is recorded as far back as 4500 BC. Their task was commercial and involved the recovery of shellfish, pearls and sponges. Records also provide us with details of Aristotle's description of the first diving bell in 332 BC, which states: 'Often, indeed, they contrive a means of respiration for divers by means of a container sent down to them. Naturally, the container is not filled with water, but air, which constantly assists the submerged man. It is forcibly kept upright, in order that it may be sent down at an equal level all round, for if it were free to incline, it would be filled at once by incoming water . . .'

History also tells us that war and military operations have played a major part in underwater developments and there are many records of diving exploits. One of the more famous was that of Issa, who served in Saladin's fleet during the Third Crusade, in the 12th century. He had constructed a breathing machine consisting of

Human exploration of the sea is recorded as far back as 4500 BC. At that time it involved free-swimming dives to recover shellfish, pearls and sponges. (Royal Navy)

War has played a major part in underwater exploits. One of the most famous early military divers was Issa, who served in Saladin's fleet in the Third Crusade during the 12th century. He constructed a breathing machine that enabled him to swim under the surface of the water. (Royal Navy)

a bellows and stones attached to a belt. During a siege he used this apparatus to swim clear of the enemy carrying documents and money, until on one of these sorties he was seen and followed by enemy soldiers in their boats. They were able to kill him when he emerged from the water.

In 1677 at the port of Cadaques, Spain, a diving bell was used to recover money from a wreck. The bell was constructed of wood with iron hoops to secure the device. Iron was also used as ballast by attaching weights to the rim of the bell. Inside, the diver had only a crossbar on which to sit. Two vessels were anchored over the wreck allowing the bell to be launched and recovered between the two. The only air supply was that which was trapped inside the bell when it was lowered from the surface. When the bell reached the bottom, the diver left the bell, dropped down to the wreck and collected as much coinage as possible while holding his breath. He then returned to the bell with the coins, hung them in bags inside the bell, and, equally important, drew breath. When the air in the bell became exhausted and stale he pulled on a rope that was secured to one of the support vessels. This was a signal for the bell to be recovered. Once the bell had been pulled out of the water another diver would enter it and, with the air replenished, descend to the wreck to continue the operation.

The famous astronomer Edmund Halley transferred his thoughts from outer space to inner space when he designed and constructed a bell with a difference. The bell itself was made from wood with iron hoops to secure it and it used lead weights

The bell used in Spain in 1677 to recover money from a wreck. It was constructed of wood with iron bars to add strength. The diver did not have any breathing apparatus, but worked in and under the bell until the air trapped in it was exhausted. (Royal Navy)

for ballast. It transported divers to depths of up to 18 m (60 ft), and had an air supply that would support them for up to 90 minutes. The innovation was in the way fresh air was supplied to the bell, which involved the use of barrels containing air. They were weighted at the bottom so as to ensure that they did not float, and were lowered down from the support vessel to a position below the bell. One end of a hose was attached to each barrel while the other end was unconnected. That end was taken to the inside of the bell so that when a tap was opened, air flowed from the barrel into the bell. Providing that the divers did not go much beyond the depth of the bell they were able to breathe the air that was supplied through a hose from the bell.

There were still problems with the

design of diving helmets but John Deane took a major step forward towards solving them. He took a helmet that had been developed by his brother for entering areas on the surface which required breathing apparatus. He modified the helmet by fitting two glass windows, a watertight neck seal and a diving suit. Once he had a prototype he took the suit and helmet and tested them by walking into the sea. On this first experiment air was pushed from the top of the suit to the legs which caused him to turn upside down. He rectified this problem by developing lead-soled boots. He then developed his basic helmet design by producing a copper helmet that allowed him to turn his head. It included three windows. Air was pumped from the surface to the helmet through a hose, and it escaped from beneath the rim. He had not developed a fully enclosed diving apparatus, but his apparatus was the best available and he was employed to dive on the wreck of the *Royal George*.

A major milestone in the development of diving and diving equipment was reached through the efforts of Augustus Siebe. He had arrived in Britain in 1816, the year following Napoleon's defeat at Waterloo, and had worked in London as

Left In 1820 John Deane took a helmet which had been developed by his brother, inserted two round windows in it and added a watertight diving dress that sealed to the helmet. Although it was not entirely successful, it could be argued that his apparatus was the first closed diving suit. (Royal Navy)

Far left Halley's Bell was constructed in 1690 of wood with steel bands and lead ballast. As the bell was lowered, air was trapped inside it, allowing the divers to breathe. The air was replenished by using two weighted barrels which were lowered below the bell and a hose allowed air to flow from them into the bell. (Royal Navy)

The standard diving dress has remained at the forefront of deep sea diving since the 1800s. It was used in the offshore oil and gas industry during the 1960s but was not flexible or efficient enough to continue in use. Although it has been overtaken by new equipment, it is still used for inshore civil engineering work in many overseas countries. (Royal Navy)

an inventor. His first attempt at developing an underwater suit followed on from John Deane's experiments and his successful open diving apparatus. Siebe improved upon this and his first system comprised a metal helmet attached by rivets to a jacket extending below the waist. Air was supplied through a hose from a pump on the surface to the helmet and then escaped from the bottom of the jacket. The user could only stand, for if he leaned forward the helmet would fill up with water.

In 1837 Siebe designed and produced

his 'closed' flexible diving dress. This new apparatus was a one-piece suit, with shaped rubber cuffs making a watertight seal at the wrists, and a rubber collar at the neck which was formed to meet the shape of the metal corslet. The metal helmet was locked on to the corslet by an eighth turn interlock system. The suit was completely sealed allowing the diver to bend over without flooding problems. With the suit, the diver wore special lace-up boots, each weighing 8 kg (18 lb), plus front and back weights which were hung over the corslet and weighed 18 kg (40 lb) each. A team of men on the surface helped the diver get into his apparatus and enter the water. They then manned a hand-pump that supplied air through a hose to the helmet.

At the same time Sir Charles Pasley of the Royal Engineers was working with underwater explosives on a project to destroy two wrecks in the River Thames. He had to contend with two major problems. The first was producing a reliable fuse that would work underwater; the second was the placing of the charges in the swift-running river. The first problem he overcame by developing a sealed waterproof charge and a special reliable fuse; the second problem of how to place it was solved by Augustus Siebe's new diving dress.

So successful was the combination of the Royal Engineer divers and Siebe's div-

The standard diving dress was used by both civilian and military divers. These Engineer divers in 1859 work from a pontoon. One diver sits ready in case of an emergency while engineers man the other diver's hand pump and hose. (Royal Engineers)

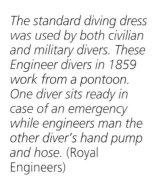

ing dress that Pasley was called to London, where he was given the Freedom of the City in recognition of his exploits on the two wrecks. Those developments did not go unnoticed, and he was appointed to the task of removing the wreck of the *Royal George*, which was fouling the anchorage at Spithead.

The *Royal George* was a ship of 108 guns whose keel had been laid in 1746. It was sunk at Spithead in 1782. Eleven hundred persons – men, women and children – had been on board, of whom only 200 were saved.

During 1782 and 1783, Mr William Tracey tried to salvage the ship. His plan was to pass cables round the lower part of the hull with either ends secured to ships on the surface. The cables were to be hauled taut when the tide was at its lowest and await the flood tide to come. This would raise the lifting ships, placing an equal strain on the lifting cables. In theory this should have lifted the wreck clear of the seabed and allowed the ships to move to shallower water where the wreck would be grounded on the seabed and the lifting process could be repeated. By continuing the process the wreck could be moved to shallow water where any damage could be made good, enabling the ship to be refloated.

To place the cables, divers and a diving bell were used, but it was a major task using unsuitable underwater equipment. The greatest problem encountered involved the divers, who were required to use leather pipes, strengthened by wire, to obtain their air supply. These pipes were subjected to external water pressure that squeezed the pipe, impeding a clear flow of air and making it difficult to breathe. This was just one of many problems and resulted in the salvage operation being a failure.

By 1839 the wreck had become a serious danger to the anchorage and the decision was made that it had to be removed. This allowed Colonel Pasley to involve his Sapper and Miner divers, using Siebe's closed diving dress, to work on the wreck. The first task was to clear the wreck of debris using explosives and lifting ropes. In this part of the operation they were

able to recover seven brass cannon, 16 iron cannon, copper and other metals. There was also a quantity of timber beams, a large volume of other items, many of them of a personal nature, and the skeletons of those who perished. The successful removal of the *Royal George* firmly established diving as a paramount factor in future underwater operations, opening the door for innovative designers and engineers. Siebe's closed diving dress, developed in 1837, is still in use in the 1990s.

Although they were limited by today's standards, divers could descend to the depths, air being provided through a hose. However, there were work tasks where being connected to the surface could be a

The Rouguayrol-Denayrouze apparatus was developed in 1872 and comprised a close-fitting suit and a hood with a metal-framed window. Air was supplied from a compressed air system that included an automatic demand valve. (Royal Navy)

restriction and impose limitations. By 1872 Benoit Rouguayrol, an engineer, and Lt Auguste Denayrouze had developed a semi-self-contained air diving apparatus. In normal operations the air was pumped from the surface through a hose to a metal canister which the diver carried on his back. The air was held under pressure and that meant that the hose could be disconnected for a limited period, allowing the diver freedom of movement. Part of the apparatus was a 'regulator' that required a membrane to separate the canister and the breathing hose. It was subjected to air on one side and water on the other, with the air side at a lower pressure when the diver took a breath. This action caused the membrane to flex and open a valve allowing more air in. When the diver exhaled the valve closed and the air passed through a one-way valve. This was the first valve that automatically adjusted to the pressure between the air inside and the water outside.

In 1876, Henry Fleuss began development of an oxygen rebreathing device that freed the diver from dependence upon surface support. The Fleuss device used a watertight rubber face mask connected by breathing tubes to a copper tank filled with oxygen and a breathing bag. The diver would inhale pure oxygen. His exhaled breath would pass into the breathing bag and there be drawn through rope yarn that had been soaked in a solution of caustic potash. This chemical absorbed the carbon dioxide, and allowed the unused portion of oxygen to be recirculated through the face mask. In the early models of this apparatus, the supply of fresh oxygen was controlled by the diver with a hand valve.

Fleuss successfully tested his apparatus in 1879, first in a tank of water where he remained for about an hour, and then by walking along a river bed at a depth of 5.5 m (18 ft). During this dive Fleuss, who had an insatiable curiosity, wondered what would happen if he turned off his oxygen feed. He soon became unconscious and suffered gas embolism as he was hauled to the surface by his tenders. A few weeks after his recovery, Fleuss made arrangements with Augustus Siebe's div-ing equipment company to put his recirculating design into commercial production.

The equipment was tested to its limits by Alexander Lambert in 1882 when a tunnel under the River Severn was flooded and required a door to be closed. The problem that faced the conventional air diver was the distance to be travelled hauling an air hose. There was a vertical shaft of 60 m (200 ft) with 15 m (50 ft) of water at the bottom. Then there was the tunnel, 300 m (1,000 ft) long, all of which was in pitch darkness. The diver reached the bottom of the shaft and groped his way along the tunnel to find the problem. The door was wedged by two rails running over the sill. He managed to rip one up with his bare hands, but the other would not move. Lambert then retraced his steps back along the tunnel to the shaft where he collected a crowbar. He returned to the door and managed to lever up the rail and force the door closed. Three years later the tunnel flooded again, and Lambert returned down the tunnel to repeat the operation and close the door .

During early 1917, at the height of the First World War, the 15,000 ton White Star liner *Laurentic* departed Liverpool bound for Halifax, Canada. The ship had been taken over by the Admiralty and converted into an armed cruiser. This journey was important as a valuable cargo of £5 million in gold bullion was on board, part of funds used to pay for armaments.

The ship was heading down past Southern Ireland when it struck a mine, and sank in 40.2 m (132 ft) of water. The loss was critical for the Government and a salvage operation was ordered.

The location of the wreck was exposed to the full fury of the North Atlantic weather so a large vessel was needed which could be moored in position to make a stable diving platform. The divers would use Siebe standard diving equipment and motorized air pumps rather than hand pumps, as diving could be continuous. A decompression chamber was carried on board so that decompression illness (the bends) could be treated, and this was of benefit to the operation because the divers knew they could there-

Alexander Lambert used the first autonomous oxygen apparatus to undertake a dangerous dive into the flooded Severn Tunnel so that he could close a door. (Royal Navy)

fore take risks that they otherwise would not have been happy to take.

The first diver to descend to the wreck provided the initial report that the *Laurentic* was lying at an angle of about 60°, which meant that the divers could not stand on the deck but had to hold on in order to move about.

It was known that the gold was stowed in the second-class baggage room, access to which was through an external watertight door on the port side. It was this door that the divers had to locate and when they had found it, a line with a marker buoy attached was installed. The support vessel was manoeuvred alongside the buoy, providing the divers with a fixed line direct to the work location.

The steel watertight door had to be removed and that was achieved by using explosives which blew it open and clear of the opening. The divers could now enter the passageway and reach the door of the strong-room. This barrier was soon removed and they had access to a number of boxes each measuring 304 mm x 304 mm x 152 mm (12 in x 12 in x 6 in),

weighing 63.5 kg (140 lb) and containing gold worth £8,000. The boxes were heavy as well as awkward for the divers to handle when moving up sloping passageways. They recovered the boxes while the access was easy but the pounding seas caused the wreck to collapse and what had been a relatively easy task now took a turn for the worse and required the divers to enter by a different route. (The complications inside the wreck caused by the poor weather conditions caused a job that should have been completed in a few weeks to take seven years.)

As with most salvage operations, the *Laurentic* was not without incident, and one of the most notable occurred while a diver was moving a heavy steel plate using lifting equipment from the surface support vessel. When removed it allowed the diver access underneath so that he could place an explosive charge. During this operation, the rigging failed and the steel plate fell, trapping the diver. He called to the surface for them to provide as much air as possible and to send another diver down with some urgency.

Those on the surface opened the valve to increase the air supply to the diver, but they were concerned that the volume of air would be greater than that which could escape through the exhaust valve on his helmet and the sheer volume of air could blow open the diving suit. Balanced against that, they did not know if the suit was damaged, allowing water to enter, but the air supply was keeping it out of the helmet. Communication was impossible due to the noise of the air entering the helmet. Because of their concern, they made a decision to reduce the flow of air in order that they could speak to the diver. When they had reduced the noise they heard the diver asking in a calm voice for more air.

The second diver was soon at depth and attached a wire to the plate. He then ordered the surface to take up on the wire, moving the plate clear of the trapped diver, who was unharmed. When back on the surface support vessel he explained that he had requested more air as the inflated suit seemed to take some of the weight of the plate off his body and make it easier for him to breathe. The fact that the suit could have burst causing him to drown had not occurred to him.

Operations continued until gold bars worth £800,000 had been recovered, but it was to be 18 months before divers returned and were able to recover more gold with a value of £470,000. As with many salvage operations, the first phase found gold without too many problems, then it required a lot of effort to recover only small quantities.

After five years had passed, £1,500,000 worth of gold bars had been recovered, with the best day of recovery bringing gold worth £150,000 to the surface. With the search restricted to odd bars, a competition was created and in one case a diver recovered gold worth £45,000 in one dive and received a tin of cigarettes as a prize! The salvage operation was a success and accounted for 99% of the gold at a cost of 2-3% of its value, and that with no serious accidents or loss of life to the divers.

During 1924 the US Bureau of Mines and the US Navy pooled their resources to sponsor a series of experiments in the use of helium–oxygen mixtures as a diver's breathing gas. The initial work was done at the Bureau of Mines Experimental Station in Pittsburgh, Pennsylvania. In 1927 the Navy shifted the operations of its own Experimental Diving Unit (EDU) from Pittsburgh to Washington, D.C. where the work continued.

The first tests showed no detrimental effects on animals or humans from breathing a helium–oxygen mixture. The principal physiological effects noted by all divers when using helium–oxygen were the increased sensation of cold caused by the high thermal conductivity of helium and the 'Donald Duck' effect on human speech that resulted from the acoustic properties of the gas.

The depth advantage to be gained from the use of helium was soon well established. In 1937, at the EDU, a diver wearing deep-sea diving dress with a helium–oxygen breathing supply was compressed to a simulated depth of 152 m (500 ft) in a compression chamber. He was not told the depth, and when asked to make his own estimate he reported that it felt like 30 m (100 ft). During decompression, at the 91 m (300 ft) mark his breathing mixture was switched to air, and he was troubled immediately by nitrogen narcosis.

In other countries, where the availability of helium was more restricted, divers experimented with mixtures of other gases. The most notable example is that of the Swedish engineer Arne Zetterstrom who worked with hydrogen–oxygen mixtures. The explosive nature of such mixtures was well known, but it was also known that hydrogen would not explode when used in a mixture of 4% oxygen. At the surface this percentage of oxygen would not be sufficient to sustain life. However, at 30 m (100 ft), the oxygen partial pressure would be the equivalent of 16% oxygen at the surface. Zetterstrom devised a simple method for making the transition from air to hydrogen–oxygen without exceeding the 4% oxygen limit. At the 30 m (100 ft) level he replaced his breathing air with a mixture of 96% nitrogen and 4% oxygen, and then replaced that mixture with hydrogen–oxygen in the same proportions. In 1945, after some successful test dives to 110 m (363 ft), Zetterstrom reached 160 m (528 ft). Unfortunately, a misunderstanding on the part of his topside support personnel resulted in a too-rapid return to the surface. Zetterstrom did not have time to enrich his breathing mixture or to decompress adequately and he was killed by the effects of the ascent.

Although open, pressure-balanced diving bells have been in use for several centuries, it was not until 1928 that a bell appeared which was capable of retaining internal pressure when raised to the surface. In that year Sir Robert H. Davis designed the Davis Submersible Decompression Chamber (SDC). The vessel was conceived as a method of reducing the time a diver would be required to remain in the water during a lengthy decompression.

The Davis SDC consisted of a steel cylinder with two inward-opening hatches, one on top and one on the bottom, capable of holding two men. In operation the surface-supplied diver was deployed over the side in the normal way, and the bell was lowered with a tender inside to a depth of 18 m (60 ft) with the lower hatch open. Surface-supplied air was used to ventilate the bell and to prevent flooding. The diver's deep decompression stops were taken in the water, and upon arrival at 18 m (60 ft) he was assisted into the bell by the tender. The diver's gas supply hose and communications cable were removed from his helmet and passed out of the bell and the diver climbed inside. The lower door was then closed, and the bell was lifted to the surface and on to the deck of the support vessel. The diver and tender remained inside the bell and were subsequently decompressed within its safety and relative comfort.

The increased decompression times associated with mixed-gas diving and the need for added diver comfort resulted in the design of an improved bell system in 1931. Davis designed a three-compartment deck decompression chamber (DDC) to which the SDC could be mechanically mated to permit transfer-under-pressure (TUP) of the diver. The DDC provided additional space, a bunk, and food and clothing for the diver's comfort during the lengthy process of decompression. This procedure also freed the SDC for use by another diving team to enable continuous diving operations.

The milestones described here show some of the foundations of the developments in diving. There was the diving bell that allowed divers to work close to a safe refuge because man underwater is in an alien environment and requires an artificial means to breathe. This was provided by masks and helmets, which kept water out and allowed air in. The helmets were then connected to watertight suits, enabling divers to remain underwater for longer periods. Air supplied from the surface had been the breathing medium, but the development of the pressure cylinder meant that divers could carry air with them and be self-contained. The volume of air that could be carried was limited, but the introduction of oxygen for diving could be used on a closed-circuit system, allowing the diver freedom of movement with no attachment to the surface, though he was still restricted by the depth to which he could go.

R. H. Davis developed the Davis Submarine Escape Apparatus (DSEA), which as the name implies was intended to be used by submariners if they needed to abandon a stricken submarine. It had three purposes: first, it had to be easy to fit without the need of assistance, second, it allowed the wearer to breathe underwater, and third, it acted as a life-jacket once the wearer was on the surface.

Because it would be worn inside a submarine it had to be as compact as possible. It was comprised of a rubber breathing bag in which a carbon dioxide (CO_2) absorbent canister was fitted. An oxygen cylinder supplied the bag, and a single corrugated tube with a mouthpiece at one end was connected to the canister at the other. The wearer breathed in, drawing oxygen from the bag, through the canister, up the tube and into the lungs. The reverse process occurred when the wearer breathed out and the expired breath passed through the absorbent where the CO_2 was removed.

When it was in use, the wearer could not race to the surface but needed to rise in a slow and controlled manner otherwise there could be damage to the lungs. The apparatus was fitted with a flap, or check vane, which could be unrolled and held out at arm's length to create a brake. Once on the surface the wearer had support from the emergency buoyancy bag which would keep him afloat, face up.

This successful item of equipment again placed Davis and the company Siebe Gorman at the forefront of diving equipment technology. The principles of the DSEA have remained into the 1990s for closed-circuit underwater breathing apparatus.

Chapter 2

Atmospheric Diving Suits

THE FIRST SUCCESSFUL atmospheric diving suit (ADS) was designed and built by John Lethbridge in 1715. In his determination to recover sunken treasure his thoughts turned to developing a machine that would allow him to descend and remain underwater, but leave his hands free to pick up the valuable finds.

He based his machine on the barrel concept, that is, wooden planks held together by iron hoops. Two attachment points on the top allowed it to be lowered and recovered whilst he lay in a prone position inside. His arms protruded through two holes that had special seals fitted so as not to allow water to enter. His face was next to the view port, which allowed him a limited amount of vision. In this device he was able to remain at a depth of some 22 m (72 ft) for about 30 minutes, after which time he had to be recovered to the surface to allow attendants to pump air into the machine, using bellows. If he went deeper, the force of the water pressure on the seals on his arms became so great that it stopped his circulation and rendered him unable to work, but within these depth limitations he was extremely successful in his underwater exploitation.

Probably the first completely armoured and articulated diving dress was designed by W. H. Taylor in 1838. It had flexible

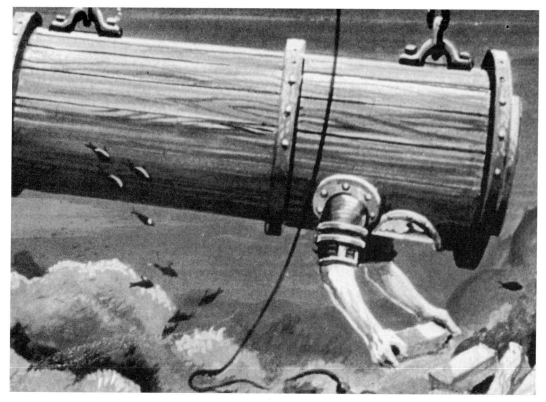

An atmospheric diving suit designed, built and operated by John Lethbridge in 1715. Constructed of wood on the barrel concept and leather to seal the arms, it allowed him to remain underwater at about 22 m (72 ft) for up to 30 minutes. (Royal Navy)

articulated joints possibly made of leather with metal rings to stiffen and keep the material clear of the operator's arms and legs when underwater. The suit was not complete in that the feet and hands were unprotected apart from leather gloves and boots. This meant that parts of the body would be exposed to pressure at depth, and it is not known how well the articulated joints stood up to pressure.

The first suit which encompassed the entire body in steel was designed by L. D. Phillips in 1856. It was comprised of a steel cylinder with domed top and bottom. Fitted to the bottom dome were two armoured legs, which had ball and socket joints. Metal arms with similar joints were fitted to the main cylinder, and each had nippers at the end which the operator controlled from the inside. Entry was made through a manhole in the top dome which was secured by nuts and bolts once the operator was inside.

The pressure of water on the joints caused the inventors of armoured suits the most problems, because a joint was comprised of movable parts. The pressure pushed the parts together so that at best they were difficult to move, and the deeper underwater the joint went, the greater the pressure, until the point was reached where the joint would not move at all.

In 1913 the firm of Neufeldt & Kuhnke developed a ball and socket joint where ball-bearings were placed between the two halves. It was kept watertight by a rubber seal which used the water pressure to obtain and maintain a seal. Neufeldt & Kuhnke used these joints when they produced their first armoured suit in 1920. The body was formed in two parts that bolted together, and fitted to it were the arms and legs. This meant that the operator's entire body was encased in steel. Whereas other suits had relied on air being supplied from the surface, the Neufeldt & Kuhnke suits were self-contained, with oxygen carried in cylinders fitted to the outside of the suit. The suit had a flotation tank at the top which could be deballasted using air from compressed air cylinders which were also carried on the outside of the suit.

As far as armoured suits up to that period were concerned, these were the most successful, but even they had limitations, for the 12 joints were susceptible to leaks. Nevertheless, the later models were used down to depths of up to 122 m (400 ft). Another vital development which extended their operating time underwater was the introduction of a regeneration system to clean the breathing atmosphere of carbon dioxide.

The oceans have held, and still do hold, many treasures, and the major underwater exploits through the ages have been undertaken for either military or salvage purposes. The biggest problem that all underwater salvage operations encountered was the limitation on the depths to which people could be put, even if they were only needed for observation purposes. So, if putting a diver down to greater depths was impossible, innovation moved to the forefront for salvage operations in deep water.

Deep-sea salvage provided a challenge, particularly if the wreck was beyond the working depth of a diver. One such vessel was the P&O liner *Egypt*, which was steaming through thick fog en route from London to Bombay when it was in collision with the French cargo ship *Seine*. As a result, the *Egypt*'s side was torn open, allowing the sea to enter and sending the ship to the bottom in about 20 minutes. The *Egypt* settled in some 122 m (400 ft) of water with a cargo of gold, silver bars and coins with a value at the time of £1,045,000.

The Italian salvage company Sorima (an acronym of Societa Ricuperi Maritimi) attempted the impossible task of locating the wreck of the *Egypt* in a vast expanse of water, and succeeded. Using Neufeldt & Kuhnke atmospheric diving suits, they were able to put observers down to examine the wreck in some detail and, most importantly, confirm the identity of the ship. The suits were also used to enter the vessel and recover the captain's safe.

Although the atmospheric suits, or armoured suits as they were known, were used on the first visit, there were so many problems with using them in deep salvage that when the company returned to the wreck, they replaced them with an observation chamber. This had been designed by R. H. Davis, a member of the British underwater engineering company Siebe Gorman. It was a cylindrical tube with an access hatch on the top. It was lowered and recovered by a wire cable, but buoyancy could be controlled by the observer inside using a ballast tank. Compressed air, used for blowing water out of the tank, was carried on the outside of the chamber.

Observation ports provided the occupants with a limited view of their external surroundings, enhanced by the addition of underwater lamps fitted to the outside of the chamber. There was an electrical power supply cable and a telephone cable, the latter providing the observer with communications to the surface support vessel. The observer would soon use all of the good air inside the chamber and so a regeneration system was fitted which removed carbon dioxide and replenished the oxygen.

The plan was to deploy the chamber from the salvage ship *Artiglio* to a location where the wreck could be observed. Explosives were then lowered and, under the direction of the observer, placed on the wreck and made ready to be fired. The chamber was then recovered clear of the water to the deck of the surface vessel to allow the detonation to take place. Once the charges had been fired the observer would be lowered back down in the observation chamber, allowing him to direct the location of the grab. When the grab was in position the observer would inform those on the surface vessel, who would then lower it and, once it had made a grab, close the jaws. This slow but methodical operation would enable sections of the ship to be removed bit by bit until they gained access to the compartments which held the treasure, which could then be recovered to the surface. This method of operation was so successful that three-quarters of the gold and silver cargo was recovered.

By 1940, the observation chamber and grab method of salvage was by far the most successful, especially in deep water. However, other dangers lurked below the

surface and often placed both operators and salvage ships at risk, as demonstrated by the salvage operations on the steamship *Niagara*.

The *Niagara* was en route from South Africa to Vancouver, Canada, with a transit stop in New Zealand. When the ship was some 30 miles from Whangerei harbour in New Zealand, she struck a mine, but continued on her way with the intention of reaching the harbour. However, the blow was fatal, and while steaming away from the incident location she sank in 133 m (438 ft) of water. A salvage operation was vital as some £2,500,000 in gold bars were part of the cargo.

The most difficult aspect of the operation was to determine the actual location of the wreck on the seabed, while conducting the search in a minefield. The cargo was important enough for naval minesweepers to be engaged in a clearance

Divers could only reach certain depths, so the diving equipment designers and manufacturers Siebe Gorman developed a submarine observation chamber in which one man could descend and have all-round vision through a series of view ports. An external light illuminated a limited area. Inside, the observer could speak to the surface support vessel through a telephone cable. The chamber was used by the Italian firm Sorima in 1922 to direct a grab during the operation to salvage gold from the wreck of the Egypt. (Royal Navy)

operation so that the salvage task could continue. It was finally determined that the ship had sunk in an area of some 23.31 sq km (9 sq miles). By trawling a wire around the seabed the salvage team hoped to locate the wreck, so each time the wire fouled, the chamber, with its observer safe inside, was deployed to identify what had been caught.

On one such dive the chamber was lowered to a depth of 132 m (432 ft) where the observer encountered poor visibility. As he grew accustomed to the murky conditions he saw objects on the seabed that looked promising. Movement of the chamber had to be achieved by moving the surface support vessel, and although that movement was restricted it did offer a limited search capability. In this case the observer did find something, the hull of a

ship that was identified as the *Niagara*.

A survey of the wreck showed it to be lying at an angle of 70°, and a most important fact was that the location of the strong-room could be determined. This had to be entered by blowing a hole in the ship using explosives. A hole of some 18 m (60 ft) by 9 m (30 ft) had to be cut out to allow the grab access to the lower decks.

The salvage team had to endure strong gales, rough seas, poor underwater visibility and the dreaded mines that floated unseen at various depths and could in the worst case sink the salvage ship. The observers could see little from the outside of the wreck and so the chamber was lowered down into the wreck itself, which enabled the strong-room to be identified. Entry to the strong-room required the door to be blown off and again it was no mean feat that an explosive charge was lowered from the surface under the guidance of the observer and placed against the door. The chamber was recovered to the surface and the charge initiated. When the observer returned to the depths he confirmed that the door had been removed, and the team had access to the treasure. The recovery of the gold required the use of the grab, and this again proved to be successful.

The innovative design and development of armoured suits did not stop, and our history books abound with stories of endeavour. It was in 1930 that Joseph Peress developed an armoured suit which overcame many of the previous problems in a revolutionary way.

Peress's suit was different because its articulated joints were sealed in liquid, to avoid the effects of the external water pressure. It had arms and claws that were manipulated by the operator, and the joints in the legs allowed a better walking movement on the seabed. The operator in its first successful dive to 136 m (447 ft) was Jim Jarrett. Almost 40 years later, an atmospheric diving suit (ADS), as armoured suits were now to be known, was named 'JIM' in honour of Jim Jarrett. It became the first operational ADS to work in the North Sea oil and gas industry. The British company Underwater &

The man who became a leader in the development of atmospheric diving suits during the 1930s was Joseph Peress. He overcame the problems of external water pressure by designing liquid-sealed articulated joints. (Royal Navy)

Marine Equipment Ltd produced the first 'JIM' ADS and it was based upon the Peress concept, but used the latest technology. The diving contractor Oceaneering International took over the operational aspect of 'JIM' and was the driving force behind its use and further development.

The first 'JIM's had cast magnesium alloy bodies with a hinged dome containing four acrylic view ports, and it was through this dome that the operator entered the suit. Sealed inside at atmospheric pressure, he could descend to depths of up to 300 m (1,000 ft) and walk about on the seabed, carrying out all manner of tasks using the manipulators at the end of the arms. The operator is not a diver, and therefore does not require any form of decompression once the suit is recovered to the surface. He breathes oxygen through an oral–nasal mask which passes his exhaled breath through an absorbent, to clean it of carbon dioxide before allowing the oxygen back into the system and into the operator's lungs.

'JIM' normally has an umbilical to the surface containing underwater television, lights and communication cables, and the umbilical also serves to lower and recover the suit to and from the work site. If the umbilical should break or become fouled, the operator can detach it and, by dropping a ballast weight, allow the suit to float to the surface. In a worst case situation, a trapped 'JIM' operator has 72

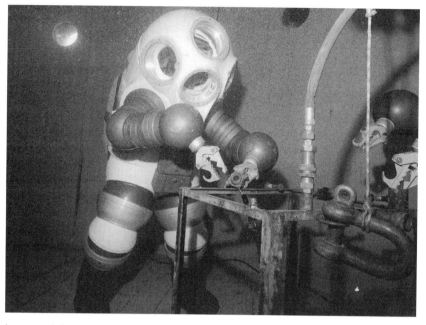

hours' life support, plus (hopefully) the knowledge that on a well-planned and well-organized operation, another ADS is available on site to come to his rescue.

Technology has progressed to develop the 'JIM' Mk 5 model, which has a body constructed of carbon fibre reinforced plastic, with limbs of aluminium alloy. The latter have oil-filled, pressure-balanced arm and leg joints that maintain freedom of movement throughout the full depth capability of the suit, and allow the operator total control over its movements. The restricted vision from the view ports has been rectified by the introduction of a

Above Based upon the Peress design, a British company produced 'JIM', an atmospheric diving suit, in 1968. It made use of modern materials and technology and was capable of working at depths of up to 300 m (1,000 ft). Man could descend to the limits of conventional diving and carry out a variety of tasks without the need for decompression. The manipulators, which are worked by the operator, are undertaking a basic work task. (Royal Navy)

Left A technician fits the articulated leg sections on to a SAM atmospheric diving suit. (Though based upon 'JIM', it did not see extensive development.) This design would allow the sections to be manufactured to various lengths to fit operators of different heights. It also means that any sections which are damaged can be replaced quickly, keeping the suit operational. (Arnold Huddy)

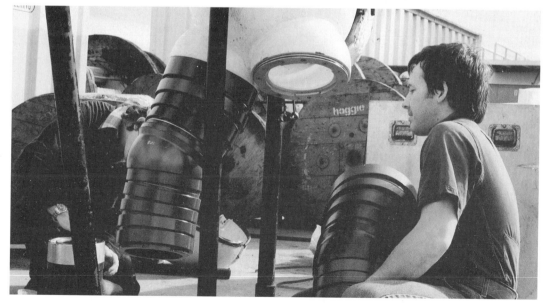

The suit opens on a hinge in the middle of the body section. The backpack cover can be seen on the back of both halves. Sitting in its handling frame the suit is ready for the operator to enter. He would do this by standing in the lower half and bending forward into the top section. With his arms in place, the top is pulled back to meet the lower section and then sealed closed.
(Arnold Huddy)

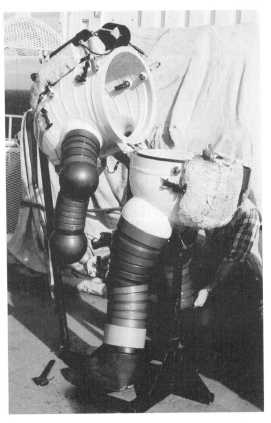

hemispherical acrylic dome providing 360° vision. 'JIM' 5 can operate to a depth of 457 m (1,500 ft). Unlike the early

models where the operators used the dome as an entry point, the modern suits have a hinged body to serve that purpose.

The atmospheric diving suit has the advantage that the operator can attend an operational briefing prior to climbing aboard. With checks completed, the suit is lifted over the side of the support vessel by crane and lowered to the seabed, where he is then able to walk to and around the job site. Communications to the surface are clear and uninhibited by the effects of helium, as would be the case with a diver.

The suit can be equipped with colour TV cameras to relay pictures to the surface. Work tasks can be undertaken using the manipulators and specially designed tools which, like the suit, have been developed over the years to allow greater dexterity. Upon completion of the operation, the suit is pulled to the surface and recovered to the deck of the vessel, allowing the operator to leave the suit and be debriefed, something the saturation diver cannot do.

The main disadvantage of 'JIM' is that it is predominantly a seabed system, though it does have an 'add-on' package of thrusters that allow it to be used in

Right *The SAM suit is ready for deployment. Smaller than 'JIM', it has a single dome port which affords the operator forward vision only.*

Far right *A 'JIM' suit is used for work on an underwater oilfield wellhead. A walkway helps the operator to walk round the equipment and makes access easier. The basic manipulators are fitted to the arms, but tools were developed for specific operations.*
(Oceaneering)

mid-water. That caused another system designer to reach for the drawing board and as a result 'Wasp' evolved as a mid-water capable ADS. This suit is also operated by Oceaneering International on a world-wide basis to complement 'JIM'.

'Wasp' does not have legs, but is based upon a cylindrical body to which multi-directional thrusters are fitted. These maintain the suit's movement and station and are controlled by the operator using foot pedals. The main body is constructed from a high-grade aluminium casting, whilst the trunk is made of a filament-wound, resin-impregnated tube casting. The arms are similar to those fitted to 'JIM', and are equipped with interchangeable manipulators or specialist tools.

The operator has a hemispherical dome for good vision, which is essential when controlling the suit's movement in a mid-water situation. The four thrusters are provided with power through an electrical cable in the umbilical, and they provide thrust in all directions, allowing the suit to be operated in up to a 2 knot current. With an operational capability of 610 m (2,000 ft), it carries a life support package for 72 hours and batteries for limited thruster operation. Oceaneering provides an ADS package which comprises a 'JIM' and a 'Wasp', which means that there is flexibility for various working operations and a rescue capability in the event of an accident.

Virtually a twin to 'Wasp' is the 'Spider', which was developed by another underwater engineering company and is operated by the diving contractor Rockwater. It has an electrically insulated GRP body and a Plexiglas hemispherical dome, and the articulated arms have powered claws capable of numerous tasks. Six variable-direction thrusters provide the propulsion, and it has the unusual device of two extending arms with suction pads fitted at the ends that allow the suit to attach itself to suitable surfaces. The operational depth rating of 'Spider' is 610 m (2,000 ft), and like all ADSes, they would normally operate in pairs, for if one becomes trapped, the other can effect a rescue. This also enables round-the-clock operations, as one can be working whilst

the other gets ready to take over, so ensuring continuity.

All three of the suits described are air transportable, which means that they can be moved at short notice to any part of the world. Then, providing a suitable vessel and dock-loading facilities are available, they can be rapidly deployed to a work site. Outside of the petrochemical industry, ADSes are used in salvage and rescue operations both military and civil-

Man and machine prepared to work underwater. The diver, wearing a Kirby Morgan helmet, hot water suit and combined bail-out bottle, weight and rescue harness, holds his umbilical. He is standing alongside an Oceaneering 'Wasp' ADS in its transportation frame. (Prodive)

Oceaneering International deployed 'JIM' and 'Spider' suits throughout their world-wide operations. This resulted in the formation of an atmospheric diving group who were identified by a distinctive badge. It portrays the 'JIM' suit.

A 'Spider' atmospheric diving suit is launched from a drilling rig. Unlike the 'JIM' suit, 'Spider' does not have legs and the suit relies on thrusters to manoeuvre. The operator has a dome port which provides good vision. This suit has an underwater television camera attached to the top of the dome port. The arms and manipulators are similar to those fitted to the 'JIM' suit. (Rockwater)

ian. It has also been found that for a number of locations, particularly those that are remote or are in deep water, ADSes are cost-effective against saturation diving techniques, which require special vessels, saturation diving systems and expensive breathing gas.

The ADSes of the '70s, while much improved and successful, suffered from limited dexterity, and in many cases in the offshore oil and gas industry, underwater structures impeded their access and ability to work. Much useful work was and still is undertaken by those early ADSes, but while they were operational a Canadian engineer was learning from their limita-

tions and working on a design that would overcome them.

The problem that had beset all designers over the years had been the joints, and while improvements had been made, it was still the case that the deeper the suit went, the greater was the pressure on the joints, with the result that they became difficult to move. There were also limitations with joints of this type on the amount of rotary movement that was available.

In Canada, Phil Nuytten developed a design for a fluid-filled rotary joint where increases in pressure had no effect on its movement. Its concept involves the utilization of external ambient sea pressure to provide a counterbalancing force that allows for low-friction rotation. Being the critical element of the suit project, the joint underwent controlled testing and refinements lasting three years. It is claimed that the resulting operational joint has 75% of the dexterity of a normal diver.

From the results of this research and development evolved the Newt Suit. It is capable of working at depths of up to 305 m (1,000 ft) and has taken the ADS to the limits of current technology, particularly in the area of dexterity, which was the greatest problem with the earlier suits. At the time of writing, 18 Newt Suits are working in various parts of the world, including in operations in the North Sea, where the Newt Suit has replaced the 'Spider' in the diving company Rockwater. It is also possible that a lighter version with a depth capability of 92 m (300 ft) will be produced, which would reduce capital costs.

Apart from the advantages of the improved dexterity, the suit can be equipped with a thruster pack. This comprises two high-speed motors with variable thrust propellers operated by the pilot with foot actions, leaving the hands free to operate the manipulators. Safety features include drop weights, an umbilical jettison and a hard wire and wireless communication system. There are two independent closed-circuit oxygen supply systems, each with a duration of 48 hours.

The applications for ADSes are unlim-

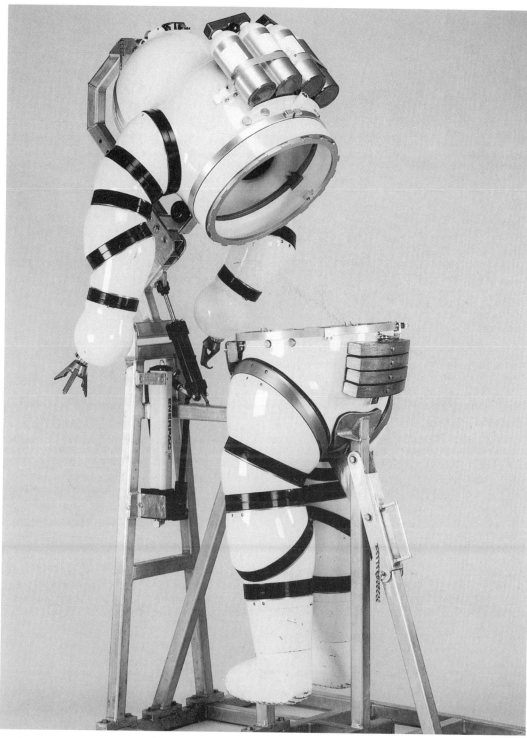

The Drager Newt Suit is divided into two sections with a watertight pressure seal. This also allows the diver access into the suit. The oxygen cylinders can be seen on the back of the upper section while emergency drop weights are seen on the back of the bottom section. (Drager)

ited, and while the offshore oil and gas industry is an obvious customer, there is also interest in civil engineering, underwater research institutions and naval operations. Interest has even been expressed by the space industry. Operational experience will prove the system design and that is well underway. One example is the use of two Newt Suits, equipped with thruster pack systems, to install concrete span correction bags underneath a gas pipeline off the coast of Vancouver. During a three-month period more than 120 dives were made down to depths of 260 m (850 ft). The average dive time was four hours with the longest dive being just over ten

An underwater view of a Newt Suit at work. The thruster unit can clearly be seen. (National Hyperbaric Centre)

hours. The Newt Suit allowed the operators to take measurements of the pipeline, install grout bags under the pipeline and pump the bags full of concrete.

Another example was when the suits were used for a ten-month project in Athens, Greece, for the installation of a 4 m (13 ft) diameter sewage outfall pipeline. The work included general inspection, removal of damaged parts, undertaking grout repairs and using hydraulic wrenches and grinders, all of which was undertaken without the need for major adaptations to the suit or its equipment.

As long as there is a need to put man underwater there will be a need for equipment to provide support. Atmospheric diving suits are one answer, as they are able to allow easy access to depths beyond that of the diver, and even in the diving depth range, there is the advantage of not needing large and expensive diving support facilities because they do not expose the operator to the water pressures encountered by conventional divers. They will not replace the diver but will take their place alongside manned submersibles and unmanned ROVs as they provide a viable work system, allowing an operator, with good clear vision, to make value judgements not afforded to other vehicles.

Chapter 3

Commercial Diving

IN THE EARLY 1960s divers were required to support the offshore exploration for oil and gas, which required them to dive deeper than was generally expected of commercial divers of the time. They were often required to dive at very short notice, in the extremely bad weather conditions generally found in the North Sea. Their diving equipment consisted of standard diving dress in some instances, while others wore wet suits and used scuba (self-contained underwater breathing apparatus) equipment. They came under pressure from their companies, who had commercial considerations, as well as from the rig's tool pusher who wanted the work done so as to keep the rig operational, and to free valuable beds for those considered more important. In addition, divers had to contend with a range of equipment that was generally unsuitable for the new offshore work sites. There were very few divers or supervisors who were trained to carry out these diving operations. There were no diving schools, consequently most divers either came with inland diving experience or were former military trained divers. Of the latter, some had been diving instructors and senior staff with supervisory experience for open water and deep diving, but for many, it was a case of learning as they went, with the result that the accident and death rate was very high.

In the early days of offshore exploration in the UK the only diving legislation in

Below left *The standard diving equipment developed in the 1800s was used in the mid-1960s when the North Sea oil and gas exploration began. Divers were transported to and from the water, a distance of some 18 m (60 ft), in an open basket. The standard equipment had an excellent track record for reliability but it was not suitable for the offshore industry's requirements.* (Mark Neild)

Left *In the late 1960s diving support to the new North Sea offshore oil and gas industry was limited. Diver Laurie Duffin shows the limitations of a one-man decompression chamber. A diver could be placed inside for treatment in an emergency, but it would not be possible to provide medical aid. These small chambers were soon replaced by larger, twin-lock chambers, which allowed medical support access to a diver already inside.* (Laurie Duffin)

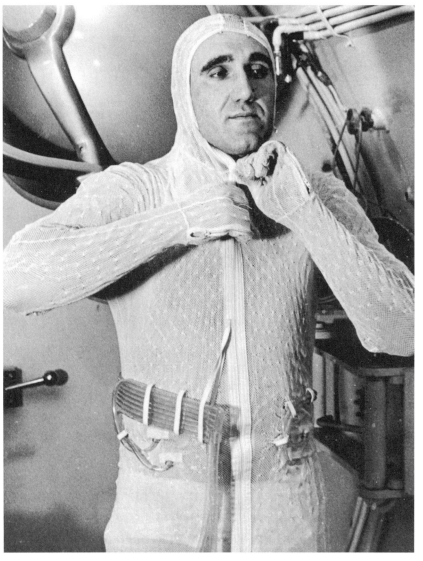

Keeping warm while underwater is important for divers, who may have to work for several hours. Woollens can be used under a dry suit and hot water suits play a major part in modern diving operations. Through the years there have been many experiments with diver heating systems. This one comes from 1971 and is an electrically heated undersuit, but due to concerns about mixing electricity and water it was never popular or adopted.
(Alain Tocco, Comex)

existence was the Diving Operations Special Regulations 1960 S.I. No. 688 issued by the Minister of Labour as part of the Factories Act. It is doubtful if the Regulation applied to the offshore industry; it is also doubtful if any of the companies involved knew of its existence. The principal guidance used by divers was the Royal Naval Diving Manual and Diving Tables and the US Navy Diving Manual and Diving Tables. The latter were preferred by the companies, as the tables gave the diver more time underwater. They were developed for their respective countries' naval diving teams, not for commercial operations, and whilst they provided guidance for the diving contractors and supervisors, they had no standing in law.

The larger diving contractors such as

Comex and Oceaneering did produce their own operational procedures manuals which gave instructions and guidance to diving supervisors and divers. Prior to 1974 there was no definitive legislation in force under which those involved with diving operations were to conduct themselves, and so the companies' manuals often took second place to commercial pressures. The client companies did not have to accept what was written and therefore based many decisions upon commercial considerations, which was not in the best interests of either the diving supervisors or the divers.

It is therefore evident that at this time there were few legal controls over diving operations, and that diving supervisors and the companies for which they worked were under considerable pressure from those who employed them. The records show that in 1971 there was an estimated diving population of 100 divers in the UK sector of the North Sea, and in that year one diver was killed. The following year there were an estimated 600 divers working in the same sector, and that year six divers were killed.

One of the problems was that the dramatic increase in the number of divers being used over a very short period meant that more diving supervisors were required, but persons with suitable qualifications and experience were not readily available. Divers were sometimes promoted to fill vacancies on the grounds of 'who they knew' rather than their ability to do the job. This was often encouraged by the onshore company management, who possibly considered that a 'yes man' would provide a commercial advantage when working offshore. This may be part of the reason for the dramatic increase in diving fatalities that occurred. Another major factor was undoubtedly the fact that many of the new divers lacked any form of training or experience. In the wake of alarmist media headlines which highlighted the high accident rate amongst divers, legislation was drawn up specifically for diving operations in the offshore oil and gas industry.

To administer this new legislation, Commander Jackie Warner, a civilian,

Underwater exploration in Arctic waters has its own problems. Breathing equipment can freeze up and divers have to endure cold water and a cold surface environment. Military divers have established a wealth of knowledge and experience of diving in hostile conditions. (Dutch Marine Corps)

became the first Diving Inspector in 1974, as part of the newly formed Department of Energy Inspectorate. His endeavours are described in a forthright manner in his book *Requiem for a Diver*. One of his first tasks was to issue a Diving Safety Memorandum (DSM) from the Department of Energy to the offshore industry. The document was not legally binding but, like those which have followed, it provided a basis for industry standards. The Memorandum clearly pointed out his concern that diving supervisors were being placed in impossible situations and that divers' lives were being put at risk. This was a clear warning to those who applied the pressure that they could be in breach of the new regulations. The DSM is quoted in full:

The offshore installations (Diving Operations) Regulations 1974 place considerable responsibility for safe conduct of diving operations on the diving supervisor and, indeed, the diver himself.

There is no doubt that, at all times, everybody involved in offshore exploration for minerals is under considerable pressure due to the vast amount of money invested. However, this situation must not be allowed to put unnecessary pressure on diving supervisors to continue operations when they

consider that conditions are unsuitable. Diving companies are requested to report to the Inspector of Diving any occasion when, in their opinion or in the opinion of the diving supervisor, undue pressure has been brought to bear to carry out diving operations which are beyond the normally accepted safe diving practices.

This was laudable in that it offered an escape route to companies and supervisors

In the water, the diver will have to endure penetrating cold, so dive times are necessarily restricted. To penetrate the ice, a hole is made which is large enough to allow access and to ensure the safety of the diver. He must have a secure lifeline, because if he becomes lost and cannot locate the dive hole, he may never surface again. (Oceaneering)

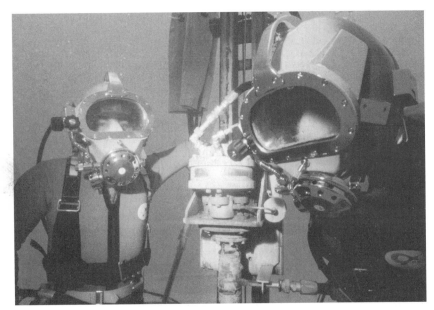

Many underwater tasks require two divers. Each diver is in contact with the diving supervisor who remains in overall command. It is possible for the divers to speak to each other through the surface communication system. (Alain Tocco, Comex)

Right *Wearing a General Electric Mk 12 diving helmet, a diver is dressed ready to enter the water. The neck clamp that holds the helmet in place can be seen, as can the umbilical attachment.* (US Navy)

under pressure, but in reality nobody was going to stand up and point the finger. A company that did would find that it was no longer asked to bid for work, and the diving supervisor who made a complaint would in effect find himself unemployable. The only way that companies or individuals were taken to task or prosecuted was as a result of an accident, when divers had been seriously injured or killed.

The exploration for gas in the southern sector of the North Sea was undertaken with the use of 'jack-up' drilling rigs. These rigs stood on legs which could be jacked up to allow the rig to be towed to various locations, and be jacked down to allow the rig to be raised into place. Because the southern sector of the North Sea suffers from very strong currents, the seabed moves and changes its profile. Therefore, the rig owners needed (and still do need) to know what the seabed was like before putting the legs down. This investigation had to be undertaken by divers, who in those days worked from inflatable boats deployed from vessels such as a supply boat. The divers used scuba equipment and had no communications with the supervisor, who generally remained on the larger vessel. The diver did a search of the seabed before surfacing and giving his report.

When the rig had moved on to location and its legs had been lowered, the bottoms would penetrate the seabed until they

reached a stable point. The rig would then be jacked up clear of the sea. Once it was stable, divers would go aboard and establish a basic air diving system. This would comprise a decompression chamber, an LP (low pressure) air compressor and very basic umbilicals. The supervisor had a small control panel from which he could provide one or two divers with air, check their depth when they were in the water and maintain communication. The divers wore all manner of masks and breathing systems, but after standard diving equipment was made redundant and scuba systems reserved for emergency use, divers were supplied with air and provided with communications through an umbilical. The task for the divers was to check the bottom of each leg to see that it was stable and establish whether the current was scouring out the seabed, which, if it was, would make the rig unstable.

The diver would be lowered into the water by means of a basket, which the diving supervisor could not see, so he relied on the diver who had been lowered

Far left *Two divers work on a sub-sea wellhead. The twin cylinders worn by each diver are for emergency purposes, as their breathing gas is supplied through umbilicals. (Alain Tocco, Comex)*

Left *Tools are difficult to use underwater and the diver will create a work platform wherever possible. This diver has to use a hydraulically powered wire brush to clean a section of a platform's leg. A basic stage is secured in place, allowing him to stand and brace himself so that he can control the tool. (Gordon Clark)*

over the side of the rig to tell him what was happening. When the diver entered the water he told the supervisor, who started the stop-watch to calculate any decompression time, although divers generally carried out 'free dive time' which did not require decompression. Throughout the dive the supervisor was exposed to the weather and general noise of the working deck area, and would also have the LP air compressor running. When the diving was completed the supervisor obtained details from the divers and provided the best drawings possible of the scour situation at each leg. If there was a problem then the divers would fill the scour hole with hundreds of stone-filled bags.

While the surface-supplied method of diving was generally found on the jack-up drilling rigs, it offered some control over the diver by the supervisor. But the tool pushers, those in charge of the rigs, often pressured the diving team to dive in extreme conditions, putting the lives of divers at risk. It was only the professional-

ism of the divers in those early days that kept the numbers of injuries and deaths from being much higher. It was to be a different story when diving began on the production platforms which were installed once gas was found.

The platforms in the southern North

A diver uses a USM2 ultrasonic flaw detector probe and unit. The reading is shown on the unit, which is read by the diver, who relays the information to the supervisor. (Rockwater)

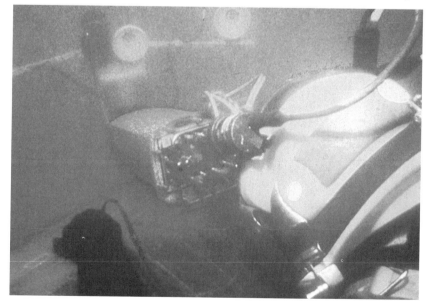

Underwater tools can be powered by air or hydraulics, but hydraulics is the more efficient system at deeper depths. The range of tools which can be used by divers is the same as that used on the surface. This diver is using a grinder and the twin supply and return hydraulic hoses can be seen attached to the handle of the tool. (Alain Tocco, Comex)

Right *Photographs provide a permanent record of inspection or damage and even today will augment any video footage. The majority of photography undertaken in the commercial sector requires cameras to be sealed in a housing to withstand the pressure of depth. For the offshore commercial application camera settings are kept to a minimum. (Rockwater)*

Sea consisted of accommodation, production and machinery modules positioned on steel legs, with strengthening bracings linking them. It became the task of the diver to clean the legs and braces of mussel growth, to check the anodes, which provided cathodic protection in order to reduce corrosion in the sub-sea section of the platform, and to look for damage. The supervisor remained on the surface while a number of divers were deployed at the same time into the sea using scuba equipment.

The divers generally carried their own air supply and were not connected by either rope, hose or communications cable to the surface. A dive ended when the diver had used all his air supply and had to surface. They may have used a depth gauge and wrist-watch to pre-determine their dive time. There was a decompression chamber on the platform but it was not generally used for surface decompression purposes, but held for emergencies.

From those humble beginnings, the UK diving industry met the demands of the offshore oil and gas companies for better-qualified divers and supervisors and for the improvement and development of diving equipment and systems. Diving schools were established and taught divers the basics of air diving and, for those more experienced, bell diving techniques. The diving industry's own professional body, The International Association of

Underwater Engineers, previously known as the Association of Offshore Diving Contractors (AODC), established a training and certification scheme for diving supervisors, for either air diving or mixed gas diving operations. They also established a scheme for life support supervisors, who are responsible for divers in saturation diving complexes.

Commercial offshore diving in support of oil and gas exploration, construction and production developed distinct operational depth limitations. There is the surface to 50 m (165 ft) band, in which divers can use air, nitrogen/oxygen gas mixture and, in recent years, oxygen/helium gas mixture, which is used for saturation diving. For depths below 50 m (165 ft) divers must breathe a gas mixture such as helium/oxygen and work from a diving bell. With such restrictions established, divers could be deployed by the safest and most cost-effective method.

In the surface to 50 m (165 ft) depth

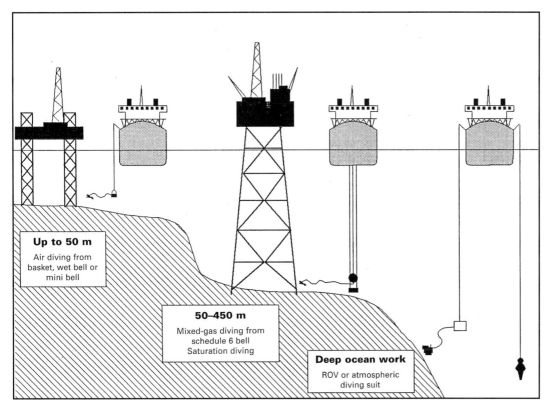

Figure 1: *Diving techniques, showing the three types of commercial diving operation which have developed in the UK. Saturation diving can extend beyond the 450 m (1,476 ft) depth, and it can also take place in depths of less than 50 m (165 ft).* (David Bray)

range, diving is generally carried out using compressed air. Historically, the vast majority of air diving has been carried out in the shallower southern sector of the North Sea, where the maximum water depth is about equal to that of the depth limit for air.

In the shallow water there is a greater movement of tidal water and therefore the southern basin of the North Sea is gener-

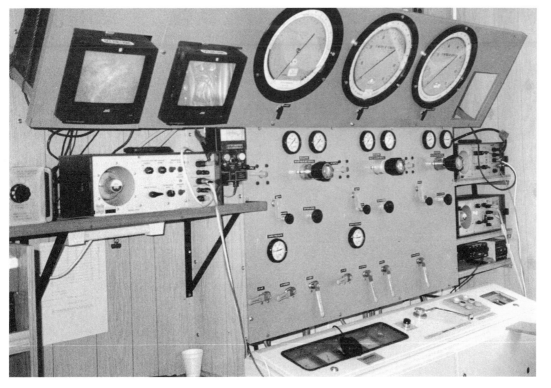

Shallow diving operations can manage with a compact diving control panel. Large depth gauges provide the supervisor with an accurate record of depth and communication is provided through independent communication boxes. The divers have hat-mounted television cameras, affording the supervisor a continuous view of their work site. (Oceaneering)

Right A tender connects the hot water hose to a diver preparing to undertake an air dive. The underwater television camera and light can be seen on the top of his helmet. The camera will relay pictures to the diving supervisor in the dive control room, who can record the entire dive on video tape.

Far right A diver wearing a General Electric helmet at work in clear water. Divers often have to work in water with no visibility at all. (US Navy)

Right An Oceaneering International triple lock air diving decompression chamber. It allows two separate decompression profiles to be undertaken at the same time. One section can allow access for other members of the diving team or medical support in the event of an emergency. Each section has its own control valves, gauges and communications. They also have a medical lock which can be identified by the black wheeled handles. Through these food, drink or medicine can be passed to the divers inside. (Oceaneering)

ally subjected to strong currents. The tidal forces flow in opposite directions, with periods of slack water in between when the tide turns and the water flow stops. This slack water period can last from half an hour to two hours or more and this occurs four times a day on an ever-moving time cycle. This has a marked effect on diving operations because, unlike saturation diving, air diving is only undertaken in the short 'no flow' periods. Because the water depth is that much shallower, the air diver has to contend with generally murky water and very limited visibility as well as the current flow. This means that, whereas the saturation diver can work steadily and methodically on a job, the air diver has to work in fits and starts and try to achieve as much as possible in the limited dive time available.

In air diving, decompression is achieved by the diver leaving the water and entering a decompression chamber at the surface to undertake his decompression profile. If a bell is not used, the diver will be exposed to atmospheric pressure for a few moments between leaving the water

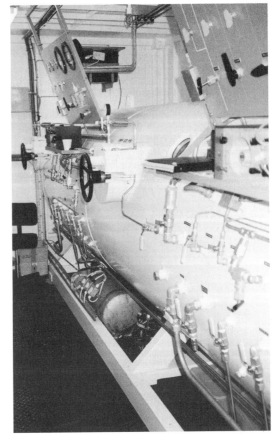

and entering the chamber. A mini bell system can be used in the surface to 50 m (165 ft) depth range, and that provides for transfer to the decompression chamber under pressure. This means that the diver does not have to be exposed to atmospheric pressure for even a few moments, and is generally thought to be safer.

The most basic and accepted method of deploying divers in the air range has been by a diving basket. This is a box frame construction with wire mesh on the sides and floor and is open to the sea. The diver stands or sits in the basket while being lowered into and recovered from the water.

Umbilicals have become an accepted part of air diving equipment. Modern diving umbilicals carry services such as a breathing gas hose, a hot water hose, communications and television cables and a depth gauge. Because of their make-up they are quite large and, as a consequence, have developed a 'drag factor'. This can be a problem when the diver goes into a platform's structure, where the umbilical passes round legs and over supporting members. Although the diver's umbilical travels from the diver to the surface, experience shows that the tender may have no physical communication with the diver and may be unable to pull the diver back to the cage unless the diver is able to assist himself, or another diver is in the water providing support. This is one valid reason for having a stand-by diver, dressed and ready to dive, on the surface, who can be deployed in an emergency.

The next development in diver deployment was the 'wet bell', which operates on the same principle as the basket, but has a section at the top which contains an air bubble and allows the diver to remove his mask or helmet, providing a safe refuge in the event of an underwater incident. Wet bell systems can be worked with the divers' umbilicals travelling from the surface through the bell to the divers. The most common practice is for the divers' umbilicals to terminate at the bell, with a main umbilical travelling from the bell to the surface. A stand-by diver can be deployed in the bell or remain on the surface ready to go to the diver's assistance in

Shackles are lowered to two divers engaged in a salvage operation while an underwater cameraman captures the event. (Alain Tocco, Comex)

the event of an emergency.

As already mentioned, safety in air diving was taken one step further with the development of the mini bell, which allows divers to be transferred under pressure to the decompression chamber where they can complete their decompression profile. This eliminates the need for the diver to undergo exposure on the surface between the last water stop and blowdown in the decompression chamber. The system has a main umbilical from the surface to the bell, and divers are supplied via individual umbilicals from the bell. As with all the other methods of air diving operation, the stand-by diver is stationed on the surface, to be available in the event of an emergency. The mini bell requires divers to descend fully dressed standing in the stage and exposed to the water, for the system does not have an outer door, and is not designed to lower divers under pres-

Air divers requiring decompression have to leave the water before entering a decompression chamber, and be repressurized to undertake a decompression profile. Ocean Technical Services, a diving contractor, developed the mini bell, which allows air divers to transfer to a decompression chamber while remaining under pressure.

being recovered to the surface and the deck of the vessel, rig or platform where they are required to remove their diving equipment and enter the decompression chamber to be placed under pressure in order to complete their decompression profile. If there is any delay in getting the diver from the water to the chamber it could have an adverse effect on the diver's health.

One of the problems facing all divers is that of being subjected to decompression sickness, more commonly known as the 'bends'. The process begins during the time that a diver is under pressure, as the body absorbs inert nitrogen gas from breathing air into the bloodstream and the body tissue. The longer and deeper the dive, the greater is the amount of nitrogen that is absorbed into the body tissue. The exact mechanism and biological changes involved in decompression sickness (DCS) are still not fully understood, but in broad terms it is caused by the inert gas, nitrogen, being released from the tissue too fast. This means that instead of being absorbed into the bloodstream and being expired into the air by the normal breathing process, it forms small bubbles within the body, causing pressure on nerve endings or blockages to the blood flow.

Continuing research into decompression sickness has caused it to be subdivided into two categories, the first of which is known as 'type one', and the second, and more serious, as 'type two'. A 'type one' case of decompression sickness occurs when the bubbles of nitrogen form in the body tissue under the skin, causing blotching and itching of the skin. If the bubbles collect in a joint area, such as the elbow or knee, a severe joint pain can be the result. The serious 'type two' cases occur when the bubbles restrict the blood supply to a principal organ of the body, such as the lungs, brain or spinal chord. With this condition, the initial symptoms vary greatly, but can develop from minor speech difficulties to unconsciousness. If treatment is delayed, the results can be fatal. Paralysis below the waist, associated with decompression damage to the spinal chord, can be a particular problem.

The accepted method of preventing

sure like the deep diving saturation bell. Upon completion of the dive the system requires the divers to enter the bell and close the door, thus sealing the divers from the outside pressure. Inside the bell the divers are maintained at the correct depth and decompression can be undertaken accurately. The mini bell is then locked on to the surface decompression chamber, allowing the divers to effect a controlled transfer without having to go to the surface first.

Decompression is a vital part of the air diver's recovery to the surface and if not carried out correctly can result in serious injury or, at worst, death. When using a dive basket or wet bell the divers undertake stops in the water at specified depths, the shallowest being 3 m (10 ft), before

*A diver working at 460 m
(1,509 ft) during the
Comex 'Janus IV' project
in 1977 off Cavalaire in
the south of France.
(Alain Tocco, Comex)*

decompression sickness is to ensure that
the diver returns to the surface pressure at
a controlled rate using decompression
tables (see Chapter 5, 'Testing the
Tables'). This should keep the nitrogen in
solution during the transfer from tissues
to the bloodstream, and until it passes
into the lungs. Decompression tables are
formulated to encompass all divers and
are based upon time durations for specific
depths.

The basic technique for diving without
the need for decompression is known as
'no stop diving'. During this type of dive,
the combination of time and depth is such
that so little nitrogen is absorbed into the
body that the diver can safely ascend back
to the surface, at a controlled rate, without stopping. If the time and depth combination is such that too much nitrogen is
absorbed for it to be released safely during
a controlled ascent, the diver must carry
out 'stops' at defined depths, determined
by the decompression tables. This will
allow the nitrogen to be expired naturally
and not form bubbles. This technique is
known as 'in-water' stops. To prevent the
diver undertaking long decompression
stops in the water, where he could be
affected by a strong current or a sea swell,
in which it would be impossible to maintain his stop depth, or by the cold water,
which could induce hypothermia, a technique of surface decompression (SUR-D)
was developed.

Surface decompression requires the
diver to be brought to the surface in a
much shorter time than would be encountered on an 'in-water stop' dive. The time
spent on the surface is very limited, only
allowing the diver time to get from the
diver deployment basket or wet bell into
the decompression chamber. Rapid
recompression then takes place to a depth
determined by the decompression tables.
This allows the diver to carry out the
remainder of his decompression in the relative safety of the chamber.

Even if decompression stops are carried
out correctly, there is still a very small
chance that decompression sickness can
occur. The only form of treatment is by
recompression in a decompression chamber. In the chamber, an attendant trained
in diving first aid and, if deemed serious
enough, a doctor, will provide support to
the diver and monitor the treatment's
progress. The treatment of a diver with

A two-man diving bell from the early 1970s, as used during the height of diving operations in the North Sea. The steel sphere is covered with thick foam which offers insulation and aids flotation. It has rubber bumpers to provide protection during launch and recovery. The bell is connected to a support stage which carried the emergency gas cylinders and bell weights. The weights could be released by the divers to allow the bell to float to the surface. This type of bell is very small by modern standards and basic in terms of the equipment carried in it.

decompression sickness is undertaken by using a therapeutic table and is supervised by the diving supervisor or life support supervisor. The urgency of the situation will require the diving supervisor and his team to evaluate the diver's symptoms quickly and start treatment before contacting the medical experts for guidance. That medical support may be several hundred miles and a helicopter ride away. Therefore the supervisor must have all the facts available so that he can ensure that the correct treatment is provided.

During both therapeutic and normal chamber decompression the diver can breathe pure oxygen, which rids the body tissue of excess nitrogen more efficiently than breathing normal air, and that in turn makes the time spent in decompression shorter. There are however risks associated with breathing pure oxygen under pressure, for a diver could sustain oxygen

poisoning, which might cause him to vomit, pass out and have convulsions. Prompt and correct action by the diving supervisor is required as delay could cause serious injury to the diver.

The length of time that a diver could remain at depth below 50 m (165 ft) and carry out any form of useful work was so limited that in commercial terms it was impracticable. Apart from the time factor, there were physiological problems associated with depth, the principal one being nitrogen narcosis, which had the same effect as alcohol, that further restricted divers' capabilities. To overcome the problems, a gas mixture of oxygen and helium was introduced. This eliminated the narcosis but still gave the diver limited time at depth. It was found that when a diver spent long periods at depth he eventually reached a point where his body was fully 'saturated' with gas and could absorb no more. It was also found that the time period of the decompression profile was the same no matter how long a diver remained under pressure.

This meant that in the deeper waters of the North Sea there was a rush to build deep diving systems which would allow divers to undertake saturation dives. In these pioneering days the early deep diving and saturation systems were controlled from one unit, entitled the 'dive control van'. During the diving phase the supervisor controlled the operation by ensuring a supply of gas to the bell and the diver, a constant flow of hot water to the divers' suits as well as the bell, and maintaining communications with all of those underwater. If there were other divers in the decompression chambers he would have to look after them as well. The launch, recovery and mating of the bell with the decompression chambers was very manpower-oriented, so he had to maintain effective control over the deck crew as well as the divers.

When divers entered saturation in the early systems, control of the decompression chamber was maintained by the dive team on a shift rotation system. This meant that during these periods the divers were not under the immediate direct control of the diving supervisor. The decom-

pression was carried out by members of the dive team, with the supervisor taking his turn on a shift or, by maintaining an 'on duty at any time' stance, undertaking a general overview of the decompression process. This meant that a new diver could be on shift, alone, with two or more lives in his hands. There were no training schools, courses or proficiency standards: the diving teams dictated the standards, with new members learning from the other, more experienced team members.

The workload on the diving supervisor during these phases of diving operations was very great, though there may have been an assistant supervisor who could help shoulder the burden. It was not uncommon throughout the 1970s for two divers to be deployed at depth for periods of between 12 and 16 hours. Throughout this time the supervisor had to remain in control of the dive and even had to have meals brought to him.

It was during this time that the North Sea became a diving Mecca, with divers and potential divers flooding in from all parts of the world. Americans, South Africans, Australians and New Zealanders were at the forefront of the invasion. It soon became common knowledge that if a diver had worked in the North Sea, he could obtain work anywhere. It also became the focal point for new diving equipment and diving systems, that were tried and tested under the arduous conditions. Anything suitable for the North Sea found favour around the world, which meant that divers working in the more remote regions had equipment which they were familiar with. Experienced diving supervisors and superintendents found themselves travelling to countries in Africa, South America, the Middle East and the Far East, their task being to organize diving operations and oversee the introduction of local divers into offshore diving operations.

Computers

Computers are playing an increasing part in undersea exploration for both the professional and amateur diver. Professional divers use umbilicals to provide them with breathing gas and other life support facilities, and rely on the diving supervisor to record the dive profile and calculate the decompression required. However, to aid this work and make it more accurate, a computerized dive profile is used. The computer is located with the diving supervisor on the surface and wires connect it to sensors which are fitted on the diver. The profiler records the time the diver enters the water, the depth throughout the dive, and the return to the surface. A paper printout can be produced to provide a permanent record. While this computerized system has many advantages, professional divers still retain the tried and tested manual methods of recording time and depth as a back-up system.

Small, programmable units are available to amateur and semi-professional divers. The data they can provide includes information on maximum depths, elapsed dive times, and decompression stops profile. All of this means that a diver can concentrate on his dive and not have to calculate the time he has spent at a given depth and the decompression required – the computer will do it all.

The next step in the development of diver computers is to enable a diver to carry a small unit underwater which will make it possible for him to communicate with those on the surface without a cable link. On land, a computer can be connected to a telephone system and data transmitted that way, but underwater the diver has to rely on through-water transmissions. The problem with sending signals through water is the interference caused by marine life, and noise underwater travels long distances, but one company may have overcome that problem.

The 'Dive Tracker', developed by Desert Star of California, is a unique system that provides navigation information, enabling the diver to locate objects as well as measure survey sites. It can also be used to obtain information on the volume of air left in the scuba cylinder, the depth of water reached at any time during the dive, and the water temperature, and it can use this data to calculate the dive profile and provide a decompression schedule. But perhaps its best feature is that it provides a communication system between the diver and surface vessel and means that the diver can obtain information from a surface-based database. All this is achieved without a cable link, relying on through-water transmissions. The system's designers had to overcome the challenge of filtering out surrounding noises which could corrupt the signal. By ensuring that the signals are clean, text and graphics can be transmitted from the surface to the divers and they can respond in return.

The unit obviously has to survive and function underwater, including coping with water pressure at depth, and so is encased in a solid block of aluminium. It has a depth rating of 305 m (1,000 ft), well beyond the depth capability of a general free-swimming diver.

The 'Dive Tracker' has a number of commercial applications, especially for scientific and research projects where a flow of information can make the work more efficient, and it could be used to advantage in salvage and military operations. However, it does have a price tag of between £1,000 and £2,000, which could limit its general availability.

Diving qualifications

Formal diving qualifications were established by the Health and Safety Executive (HSE), the UK Government's official safety body. These qualifications are unofficially recognized and accepted by many countries and companies throughout the world and can provide the basis for a skilled international diving workforce.

There is a grading system for professional divers in the UK, and qualifications can be worked for at recognized training schools. The most basic qualification is the HSE Part 4 Air Diver, which takes about three weeks to complete. This teaches a diver to use scuba gear in underwater work to a depth of 30 m (98 ft). It is suitable for engineers, scientists, and those who dive only occasionally as part of their job. Those contemplating working in docks and harbours or other inland water should qualify for the HSE Part 3 Air Diver qualification, which is more suitable for working divers. This course lasts five weeks and covers the use of scuba equipment and surface-supplied apparatus for diving to 30 m (98 ft). It is suitable for those seeking full-time employment in inland diving, where no decompression chamber is required.

There is often some confusion over the next grade, which is that of HSE Part 1 Air Diver. This is the top air diver qualification and allows the holder to work offshore in the lucrative petrochemical industry. This ten-week course provides a very intensive study of diving and includes physiology and psychology to ensure a full understanding of the subject. The trainee also uses a variety of diving equipment and tools in practical wet sessions. Diving is a means to an end, the object being to enable the diver to work safely underwater. On this course trainee divers will also learn how to operate a deck decom-

A diving instructor clamps an Aquadyne helmet in place before the diver makes an open sea training dive. (Prodive)

The storeroom of the Prodive Diving School in Cornwall, England, contains a wide range of helmets from a bygone era. On the top row are some fine examples of the old hard hat helmets. (Prodive)

pression chamber. Diving is undertaken to a depth of 50 m (165 ft), sometimes using a wet bell. This gets the diver to and from depth and also provides a safe haven in the event of trouble underwater. First aid is another vital part of diver training and is well covered in the course.

To train as a Part 1 Air Diver, a trainee can start at Part 4, then 'top up' to Part 3 and then 'top up' to Part 1, but this route takes time and may be more expensive. A trainee who is determined to make offshore diving a career can opt for direct entry to a Part 1 course. Entry to a diving course requires a medical, relevant educational standards must be met, and the diving aptitude test has to be passed.

The final diver training phase is the HSE Part 2 qualification, and that is the Mixed Gas Bell Diver. To be eligible for this course a diver will need to be a Part 1 Diver with at least one year's experience, and to have logged a certain number of dives. The training lasts six weeks and

covers the use of deep diving equipment, including oxy/helium bell diving and saturation techniques.

With the advent of the mini bell and the use of these bells in the air diving range, it was found that air divers needed additional training, although not necessarily to the standard of mixed gas saturation divers. The result was the introduction of the restricted HSE Part 2 qualification. This course lasts two weeks and covers the first module of the full Part 2 syllabus. Once a diver has undertaken the restricted course it is possible to complete the remaining modules of the Part 2 course to obtain the full Part 2 qualification.

At the time of writing, all diver training courses and qualifications are under review by the HSE, and there may well be some changes. The main aim is to simplify the basic air diving qualifications, which have led to some confusion, and to develop an international standard for all diver training and qualifications.

Chapter 4

Saturation Diving

DIVERS REGULARLY WORK and live underwater at depths in excess of 122 m (400 ft). Saturation diving requires some sophisticated equipment and a dedicated system of control. It also involves the use of a mixed gas atmosphere and breathing medium to enable divers to go down to the deeper depths. Beyond 50 m (165 ft) air causes nitrogen narcosis, which creates similar symptoms to being intoxicated. Air becomes dense the deeper the depth and it becomes harder to breathe. By using a light gas such as helium, which can be mixed with oxygen, these problems are overcome. However, even this formula of gas mix has problems in very deep diving and may require a hybrid mixture (see Chapter 5, 'Testing the Tables').

Saturation occurs when the body is saturated with the breathing gas, and it requires a defined period of decompression. Once in saturation, a diver can remain at depth for days or weeks, but he will only require the same amount of decompression. Divers live in steel chambers which are sited on a surface support vessel, not underwater as is the case with habitats, and they travel to and from the work site in a diving bell. To make life as normal as possible, each diver has a bunk, and there are toilet and shower facilities. Television is not available, but divers do take in battery-powered cassette and CD players. Those who normally smoke are unable to do so while in saturation, but once out of the chamber, they generally depart to an area where they can enjoy a cigarette. Food and other items are passed into the chamber through a small lock, which is a small chamber in its own right with a door at either end. At atmospheric pressure, it can be opened at the outside, allowing items to be placed in it. The door is then closed and secured, allowing the lock to be pressurized to a depth equal to the chambers, whereupon the divers can then open the inside door and remove the items. The procedure is reversed to pass things out.

There are numerous aspects of life under pressure, in saturation, that divers endure and take for granted. Food looks normal but has no taste. Polystyrene cups shrink to about half their normal size when subjected to pressure, causing the contents to spill out. If liquid is placed in an open container under the hole where the gas used to pressurize the lock enters, it is blown everywhere when the lock is pressurized, leaving the container empty. Cuts and sores do not heal, and in the earlier days of saturation, divers suffered from severe ear infections and open sores

The Drager hyperbaric complex shows the type of chambers that form the saturation diving systems in use aboard diving support vessels. Hatches allow divers or equipment to enter or leave when not under pressure, and divers can move from one section to another while remaining under pressure. These chambers are covered with an insulating material to maintain heating stability. (Drager)

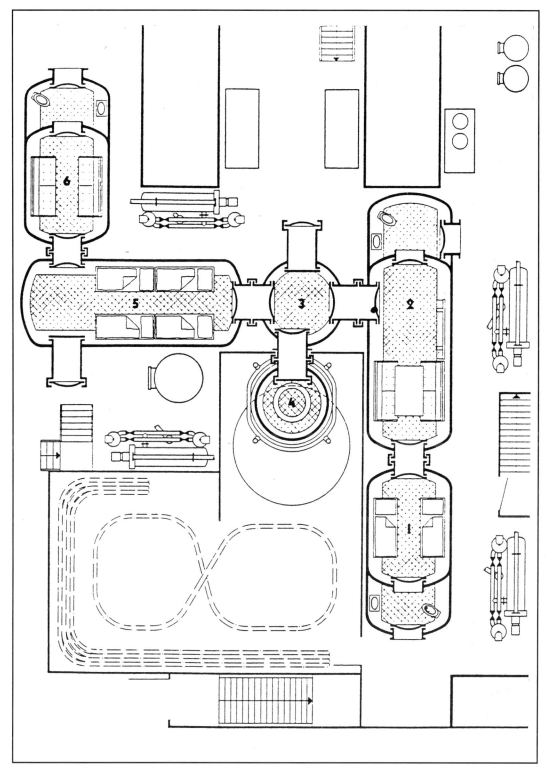

Figure 2: *The saturation diving complex layout on board the DSV Performer. Chambers 1, 2, 5 and 6 provide the sleeping and living facilities, including toilets and showers, and are linked together. Chamber 3 is the transfer lock, to which the bell connects, and allows access to the complex. Number 4 is the diving bell.* (Oilfield Publications)

between the legs and toes. Living under pressure in the close confines of a saturation chamber complex for periods of a month at a time requires one to adapt in order to get on with fellow divers. In all the time I have been involved with satura-

tion diving, I have never known an argument to end in a fight. In fact, living together in this way creates some firm working partnerships.

During the 1970s a growing number of saturation divers were killed. I was fortunate to have undertaken the majority of my saturation diving with Derek 'Spanner' Taylor. In the chamber we spent many hours debating a wide range of topics, which was interesting in itself, but this had an unusual twist because Spanner had a strong Irish accent which, compounded by the effects of helium-induced Donald Duck speech, made him sound like an Irish Donald Duck! While in the water, often carrying out difficult work tasks, I knew that reliable help was at hand if anything went wrong. We also experienced a form of telepathy which only worked while we were underwater. For example, either one of us could be in the water, and while working, think of tools or equipment that were carried in the bell. Without any verbal communication between us, the other would select that item and make it ready for collection.

Every saturation diving complex and diving work programme differs, so the number of divers in the complex at any one time will vary. Therefore, for the purpose of explaining about saturation diving, I will use the example of a nine-man diving team. This number of divers would allow for three divers to be deployed on each bell dive. In the UK, a bell dive can last for up to eight hours, so with three

teams of three divers there would be a 24-hour coverage.

It is very expensive to hire a diving support vessel with its saturation diving system, so the charterer will be very involved with the selection and work planning of the vessel and diving contractor. The client will provide representatives to monitor the operation and discuss the operational procedures with the diving superintendent. The diving superintendent is a senior supervisor who is in overall charge of the entire diving operation. He is supported by two supervisors who each work a 12-hour shift. Their task is to control the divers both while they are in the bell and when they are locked out in the water at the work site.

During a saturation diving operation, life support supervisors and technicians will also work a shift system. Their task is vital as they have to maintain the saturation system and the chamber's environment, as well as ensuring that the needs of the divers are catered for. The divers in saturation rely on those on the outside for their very existence, and that includes the transfer of food, clothing and personal items. When divers have completed their period of time in saturation they have to undertake days of decompression, and the

Figure 3: *Providing support in the North Sea, the SSV* Uncle John *has a 16-diver saturation diving complex as well as an air diving capability.* (Oilfield Publications)

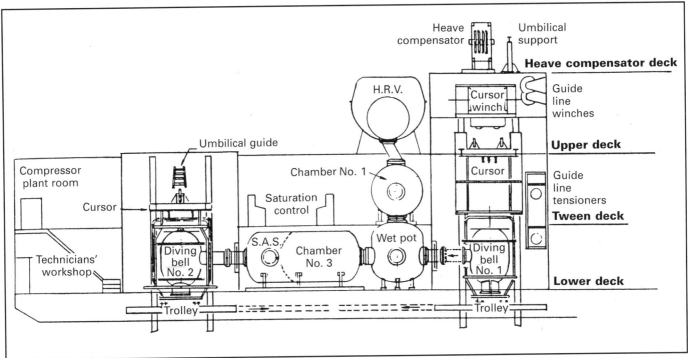

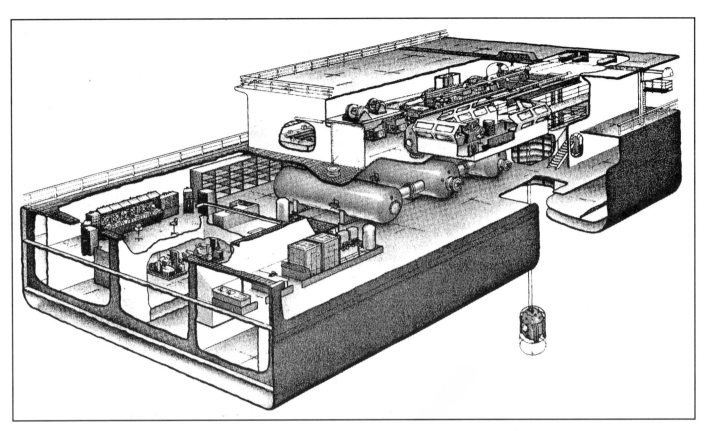

control of that profile is also undertaken by the life support team. Other divers who are not in saturation will also be available, to undertake an air dive in an emergency, or to aid the recovery of the bell in the event of a serious bell incident, such as a broken main lift wire. Saturation systems require members of the dive team to undertake the actual work of removing the bell from the system, assist with

Figure 4: *The saturation diving complex on board the* Rockwater 1 *and* 2. (Oilfield Publications)

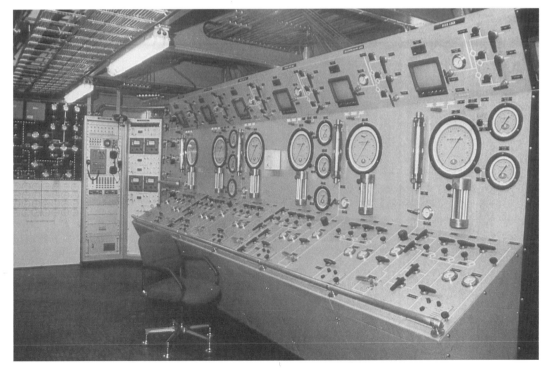

Divers in saturation rely totally on outside support. The personnel who control the life support system and functions of the complex are specialists, and are responsible for the operation and safety of those held under pressure in the chambers. The control centre has valves, gauges, communications and other instruments and is the focal point of the life support activities. (Rockwater)

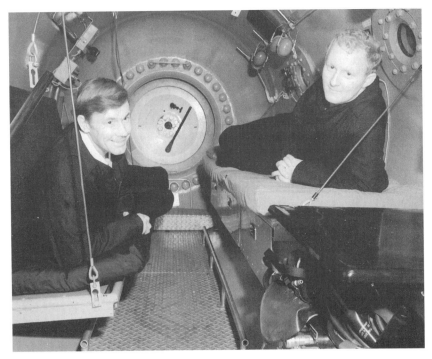

Saturation diving chambers vary in size, design and comfort, but this example gives some idea of living conditions for the divers, who may remain inside for up to a month at a time. (Royal Navy)

A diving bell in the hyperbaric complex is lowered on to the connecting flange of the decompression chambers housed on the floor below. With the faces of the bell and chamber placed together, a clamp is closed to keep them together. This is a critical part of the system as it has to hold fast under pressure. Once connected, the divers can pass between bell and chambers. (Drager)

deploying it into the water and recovering it, and locking it back on to the chamber. The degree of input differs: some systems are very labour-intensive, others require only minimal input from a surface team. These systems are so complex that they require continuous maintenance and immediate repairs in the event of a break-

down. To carry out this work systems technicians with specializations in mechanics and electrical systems are also part of the team.

Saturation divers are transported to the work site by diving bell. This is a steel capsule with hatches in the bottom to allow the divers access to the water. The bell is locked on to the saturation chamber by a mechanical device, either through the bottom hatch or, in some systems, a hatch on the side. Either of these will allow the divers to gain access to the chamber. The bell has view ports placed around it so that the divers inside can look out, although the view is restricted. They also allow a diver on the outside to look in. To aid vision when underwater, lights are fitted to the outside of the bell, but their effectiveness depends upon the clarity of the water. The bell contains a variety of equipment which makes it function and supports the three divers, both while they are in the bell and when they are out in the water.

When divers are called to dive their diving suits will be locked into the chamber system. These suits have hot water pumped into them which travels in a hose from the surface down to the bell in the main umbilical, and then out through a hose in the diver's umbilical, which is connected to the diver's suit. This constant flow of hot water keeps the diver warm whilst he is working underwater.

Prior to every dive, a number of internal bell checks have to be undertaken. They are listed on a checklist and are completed by the divers in the bell in liaison with the supervisor, who is in the dive control room. This ensures that all of the valves inside the bell are in their correct open or closed position and that the emergency gas, lighting and atmosphere cleansing units are working correctly. The emergency tool kit is checked, as are the emergency procedures and survival equipment. A satisfactory completion will indicate that, from the divers' and the diving supervisor's point of view, the bell is equipped and ready to be deployed underwater.

The divers will be briefed on the work task ahead of them and, if applicable, they will have drawings or plans locked in to them. When they have put on their hot water suits they will climb into the bell from the transfer chamber. The internal door of the bell will be closed, allowing the bell to be pressurized enough to obtain a seal. The inside door on the transfer chamber is also closed and gas is added to the chamber to seal it. This leaves a small area between the chamber and the bell which has to be vented so that the bell can be separated from the chamber. The bell is now removed from the system and transferred by its own winch and trolley system to the launch area. Saturation diving vessels deploy the diving bell through a hole in the centre of the ship, called a moon pool. It is normally kept closed until diving operations begin, when it is opened, allowing the bell to be lowered into the water.

The topside team prepares to launch and lower the bell, having carried out external bell checks using a detailed checklist. When everything is ready to go, the supervisor is informed by the topside team, and it is his decision to launch the bell. The supervisor will already have ensured that there are good communications to the bell and the diving helmets and that the correct gas mix is flowing through the main umbilical to the bell. The mixture of gasses commonly used is helium mixed with oxygen. Oxygen is needed to sustain life; helium is used because it dilutes the mixture to the percentage of oxygen that is required at depth. Equally important, it is a light, safe gas, and makes breathing easy under pressure. Its drawbacks are the vocal effect it creates and the fact that it is very cold. Because of the need for good communications while the diver is underwater, an unscrambling unit is fitted to the communication control equipment. It is only the divers' speech that is affected; speech from the surface down to the divers is quite normal.

After being disconnected from the chamber, most bells are then connected to a frame which allows the bell to stand off the seabed. This enables the divers to get in or out if it should, through an accident such as a broken main lift wire, end up sit-

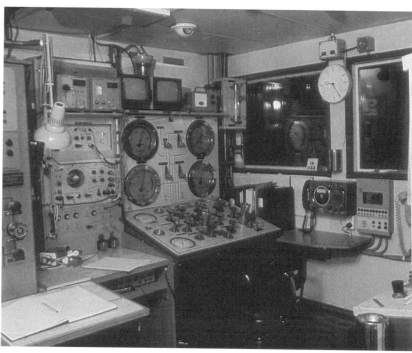

ting on the seabed. A system called a clump weight is used to stabilize the bell during launch and recovery and while it is in the water. This is a weight which is generally supported by a single wire which runs from the vessel or platform, through the clump weight and back up to a winch. For operation, the clump weight is lowered to the working depth prior to the bell being deployed. The wire is connected to either side of the bell in a way which

In complex modern diving operations, divers are supervised by a diving supervisor from a dedicated control room.

A saturation system installed on a construction barge enables diving support to be provided when required. The bell is housed in a sliding gantry that extends out over the sea when the bell is to be deployed. The side entry door on the bell allows the two units to be sealed together so that divers can transfer to and from the chambers under pressure. The side doors on the bell are sealed closed while it is in the water; divers enter and leave by a bottom door during a dive. (Gordon Clark)

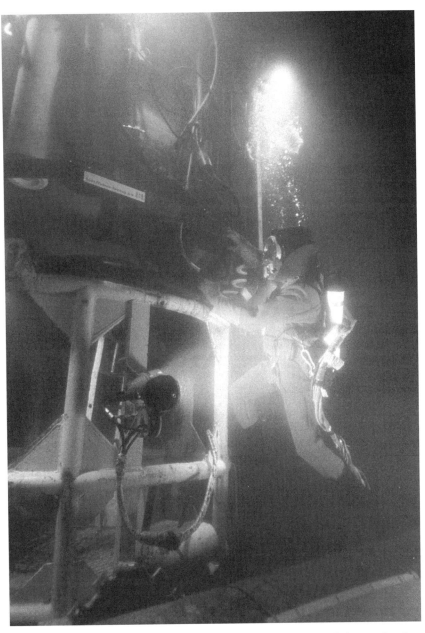

A diver outside a bell that is illuminated by its external lights. (National Hyperbaric Centre)

At night, darkness surrounds the bell, hindering vision for the divers inside. Lights on the outside illuminate the area immediately around the bell, but their effectiveness is dependent on the density of the small particles of marine life which reflect the light back. The divers may request that the lights be turned off in order that they can see more in the gloom. During daylight hours, light penetrates the depths from above and the divers are able to see, but without artificial light source there is no colour.

When the bell stops, the only noise will be the hum of the CO_2 scrubber, which removes the carbon dioxide from the atmosphere. The divers will check the bell and inform the diving supervisor that everything is ready to progress to the next phase. They will then open a valve to provide a flow of gas in order to equalize the pressure inside the bell to that outside. Once this is done, the door can be opened, exposing the divers to the water. The first diver to lock out will put on a combined harness, weights and bail-out bottle unit. The helmet will be placed on his lap whilst the umbilical is connected to the harness. As already explained, this contains hoses and cables which provide breathing gas, hot water, depth recording, communications and television camera system cables.

Two types of deep diving 'hat' are available to the diver. The first is called a band mask, and is a moulded face frame with a view plate to which a neoprene hood is clamped. A rubber holding device called a 'spider' fits around the back of the head and connects to the clamp, pulling the mask into the face and holding it secure. A neoprene face seal at the point where the hood and frame meet excludes the water, and the diver breathes through an oral–nasal mask. Sealed speakers are fitted into the hood, and a microphone is installed in the oral–nasal mask to complete the communications system. The mask is of a sound, well-proven design, is comfortable to wear, and its only drawback is the neoprene hood which allows water to enter and be next to the head. This is not a problem in warm shallower water but in cold deep water it can cause the diver some discomfort. A full 'hat' is

allows the bell to run up and down freely.

Inside the bell, the internal light illuminates the divers and their equipment. They are able to read off the depth in either feet or metre intervals as the bell descends. (It is interesting to note that the majority of diving systems and diving tables work on imperial measurements.) On the diving support vessel, the supervisor checks the bell's depth using the gauge on the dive control panel. The main lift wire winch pays out the heavy steel cable which holds the bell, while another winch pays out the umbilical which provides the operational services to the bell.

based upon the band mask frame design, but instead of using a neoprene hood, a fibre-glass shell is moulded to the frame to make a complete helmet which fits over the head. The helmet, which has an oral–nasal mask and communications, seals onto a neck seal using a clamp arrangement. This type of helmet has the advantage in that the head stays warm and dry and the communications are better and more reliable.

Diving helmets enable the diver to see what he is doing reasonably well in clear water. In dirty water and at night, however, the diver's vision is restricted, and this requires work to be accomplished by feel. This is not a new problem, as divers working in rivers and docks have always had to contend with black water conditions. It is difficult to locate objects when you cannot see them, and to work with instruments that have to be set up and operated. The solution is a new helmet system aptly named the Cycl Ops.

The system employs a silicon-intensified target (SIT) camera which is designed for depths where there is little ambient light, and it can counter the effects of suspended matter. It consists of a miniature camera and light which are fitted into the top of the helmet. Because the camera has the ability to see when a diver cannot, pictures of what is in front of the diver are transmitted to a monitor at the surface. Those pictures can then be transmitted back to the diver's helmet from the surface controller via the electronics which are housed in an extension bump on the top of the helmet, through a periscope of unique optics, to be displayed onto the miniature eyepiece monitor which sits just above the diver's right eye. The eyepiece can be altered externally to suit each individual by sliding the assembly vertically, and it can be moved clear of the diver's vision if the system is not required. The system also allows drawings from the surface unit to be transmitted to the diver. If two divers use Cycl Ops helmets, one diver can see what the other is doing, and both can be provided with pictures from an ROV.

The gas supply and return hoses, emergency gas supply hose, communications

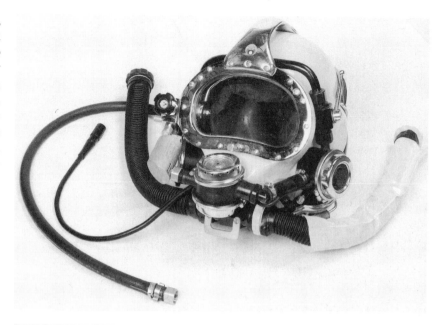

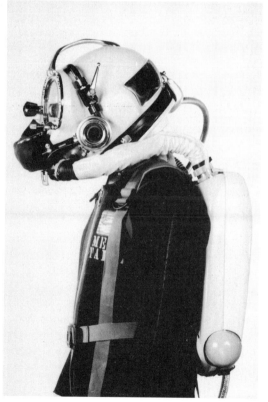

and television camera cables are connected to the helmet. The diver then checks their operation, which means he has to communicate with the supervisor. The bail-out bottle will supply gas to the diver in the event of a failure of the main gas supply and is operated by the diver by the opening of a valve on the side of the helmet.

The Drager Closed-Circuit Breathing System has been developed to make it possible for divers to descend to depths of 600 m (1,968 ft). The object of the system's helmet and bail-out facilities is to create a safe and efficient underwater unit, enabling the diver to breathe effortlessly while the exhaled gas is recovered to the surface for purification. The correct amount of oxygen is then added and the gas returned to the diver. Because of the low temperature of helium gas, the unit has a gas heater. The semi-closed-circuit bail-out backpack is connected to the helmet and provides a minimum of ten minutes' gas supply for emergency purposes. (Drager)

When all the equipment has been checked out, the first diver to leave the bell will put on his helmet. In the majority of cases this will be the full helmet, leaving the band mask to be used by the bell man in case of an emergency, for it can be put on without assistance. The hot water hose is connected to the diver's suit, and with a full flow of water he is ready to 'lock out' and enter the water.

The diver eases himself into the trunking and lowers himself into the water. During his initial immersion in the water, it will be cold water that enters the suit, to mix with the hot water and provide a good balance. Sometimes the mix does not occur quickly and cold water reaches the diver's body, particularly the spine, causing a sharp intake of breath. The water temperature is controlled by the supervisor at the surface, and the diver needs to ask for it to be hotter or cooler.

When the diver is in the water, the helmet is quickly checked to ensure that it is working correctly. The bell man then pays out the diver's umbilical, allowing him to leave the bell and swim or walk to the work site. As soon as the first diver is on location and settled, the second diver goes through the same process of preparing and fitting his equipment before he too leaves the bell.

Depending upon the type of equipment being used, the diver's expired gas can be recovered to the surface to be reused after impurities have been removed and more oxygen has been added. Before the technology to do this was developed, expired gas was simply discharged into the surrounding water, but helium gas is very expensive, so the reclaim system has become very common in order to maximize its use. Should the reclaim system break down, the diver can go on to open circuit, which allows him to breathe, and expel the expired gas into the water.

Divers are able to move freely and easily. The hot water suit is loose fitting, and the hot water pumping around their bodies makes them feel as if they are in a bath. The helmet allows them to breathe freely, upon demand. As already explained, their voices are different whilst breathing helium, and that causes problems with understanding what is being said. Although radios with voice unscramblers help, this is an area where little helpful development has occurred.

Divers communicate through a wire which is an integral part of the umbilicals. It enables communication to take place between the diver and the bell, and the bell and the supervisor on the surface. Although it is possible for two divers underwater at the same time to speak to each other, it is not common practice, and most communication links are between each diver and the supervisor. This ensures that the supervisor at the surface has total control over the diving operation, which is vital. To the uninitiated, a diver breathing helium will sound unintelligible over the radio, even using the unscrambler. The supervisor, however, develops an ear for the sound over a period of time and, knowing the work task being carried out, is able to understand. He must know what the diver is doing at any time – lives may well depend on it.

During the dive the bell man remains in the bell and monitors the flow of breathing gas to both divers as well as the temperature of the hot water. His task is basically very boring and he may well spend up to six hours sitting in the small sphere with nothing to look at. One has to make oneself as comfortable as possible, and it is not unknown for a bell man to read a book, but if anything happens to the other divers while they are out in the water, he will have to put on his equipment and go to their aid. He will be dressed in a hot water suit but does not have the bail-out bottle, harness, weights, fins or band mask on. However, in the event of an emergency he must be able to get dressed quickly without help and enter the water so that he can render assistance to one or both divers.

The bell has an electrical power supply which provides power for the internal and external lights and the carbon dioxide scrubber. The latter uses a filter with an absorbent through which the bell's gas is drawn and this removes the impurities and provides clean gas which is recirculated around the bell. The hot water which is pumped from the surface to the

Below left A hyperbaric lifeboat does not look any different from a conventional lifeboat on the outside, but inside there is a chamber capable of accommodating all the divers held under pressure. They enter through a tunnel from the main complex and, when inside, seal the internal door. Strapped into their seats, the divers can breathe through the bib masks to make best use of the available gas. This will also help if any of the divers are seasick. The lifeboat is then launched with the life support supervisor and other team members inside the boat, but outside the pressure chamber.

divers' suits also provides the basis for warm air circulation as it passes through a heat exchanger and fan. The bell is equipped with survival packs, one for each diver, in case the bell becomes totally disconnected from the surface. If that happens it will have battery power for the lights and carbon dioxide (CO_2) removal unit, but no form of heating. The divers must get into the survival bags as quickly as possible because their body heat will be rapidly drawn away, and the cold will kill them before they can be rescued.

Every bell has a transponder attached

To enable divers to remain under pressure while they transfer to the lifeboat from the saturation chambers, the chamber complex is generally positioned at a lower level than the lifeboat. A tube connects the two systems. (Drager)

lost the bell to have a second bell, or there to be another vessel with a saturation diving system in the area. The rescue bell will have all non-essential equipment removed and carry two divers. It will be lowered close to the stricken bell, whereupon one diver will lock out and take an umbilical with a band mask fitted to it to the bell. Providing the divers are in good health, the mask will be passed in, and the first diver in the stricken bell will connect the hot water hose and the mask. Both divers will then return to the rescue bell. When the rescued diver is safe inside, the diver will return to the stricken bell to repeat the exercise. He will continue until all the divers have been transferred to the rescue bell, when he will enter it as well and it will be recovered to the safety of the chamber complex of the rescue vessel. All operations are observed and recorded through the use of television cameras on an ROV. This means that in areas of the world where the correct procedures and equipment are used, deep diving has an excellent safety record.

Divers maintained in a saturation diving complex cannot just leave. They require a certain number of days to return to the surface, depending upon the depth of their dive. This means that they are at risk if their vessel, rig or barge is involved in a serious incident, such as a fire, collision or other disaster. A recent incident occurred in the Far East when a barge with divers in saturation aboard it encountered a hurricane. The barge was abandoned, but the divers were unable to leave as they had no method of evacuation. The barge sank with the divers still in the chambers, and, with no life support system, combined with the fact that the water pressure outside would eventually be greater than that inside the chambers, allowing water to enter, they died. The divers might have escaped if that barge had been fitted with a hyperbaric lifeboat. The lifeboat is part of the saturation system and has a small chamber inside which can accommodate all of the divers in saturation. It is connected to the chambers by a long tube, through which the divers have to crawl, and is maintained under pressure throughout the diving pro-

to it which emits a signal. This allows a surface vessel to use a transducer to search for the signal and locate a stricken bell. A rescue can then be planned and undertaken following proven rescue techniques. A bell has ballast weights which the divers sealed inside can drop using a mechanical device. This should make the bell rise to the surface, though a length of main lift wire and umbilical could add weight and leave it suspended in mid-water. The most effective rescue option has been to use another bell and make a through-water transfer. This requires the vessel that has

gramme. Also in the boat, but outside the chamber, is a control panel that enables the life support personnel to go with the boat, to look after the divers and effect a decompression profile. The boat carries sufficient life support facilities to be a viable rescue vehicle.

In the 1990s saturation diving systems are found on semi-submersible drilling rigs, construction and heavy lift barges. The vast majority of systems are on dynamic positioned diving support vessels (see Chapter 15), which undertake work programmes throughout the world including salvage ...

It was described as the greatest salvage adventure ever undertaken, and involved the use of a dynamic positioned diving support vessel and saturation divers. It was the recovery of more than £40 million in gold bullion from the wreck of the HMS *Edinburgh*.

The 10,000 ton cruiser left Murmansk, Russia, in 1942 carrying 465 gold bars packed in fives in wooden boxes filled with sawdust and stored in the ship's aircraft bomb room. The gold was Stalin's payment for American armaments. The loading had been done in great secrecy. On its journey through the Arctic it was spotted and attacked by the German submarine *U456*. Using three torpedoes, the submarine dealt the *Edinburgh* a fatal blow that sent the ship and its valuable cargo to the ocean floor.

Salvage of the gold was contemplated during the ensuing years, but it would have required the use of explosives and a grab and, because the wreck was considered to be a war grave, the opportunity was never exploited – not, that is, until a salvor, a diving contractor, a vessel owner and a navigation equipment company combined to work together to undertake the operation. This was done to spread the financial risk, because any returns depended upon recovering the gold, and there were other factors, namely the Soviet and British governments, who each wanted their share.

The vessel and equipment involved capital investment, but the key to the success of the operation lay firstly in locating the wreck and secondly in the divers, who were to be in saturation, work in deep water, and enter a ship amidst bombs and shells, all on a 'no gold, no pay' deal.

As with all deep ocean salvage operations, the wreck had first to be located. This required research into wartime records, which was complicated by the fact that the Russians, who stood to gain financially, refused to provide any help. The UK government were not overly co-operative as the wreck was considered to be a war grave; it is also said (though this is a point not generally known) that Royal Navy nuclear submarines used the wreck to hide behind during patrols.

Eventually agreements were signed and the survey vessel *Dammtor* travelled to the Arctic to search for the *Edinburgh*. The search of the ocean floor used a computerized side-scan sonar system, and when a large echo was made the *Scorpio* ROV was deployed. After 15 days of searching the wreck of the cruiser was located – now the salvage operation could begin in earnest.

The diving support vessel *Stephaniturm* would be the operating base for the dive team, remaining on station using its dynamic position system (see Chapter 15). The vessel had a single diving bell to transport the divers to and from the wreck, which had a certain disadvantage in that, had there been a serious incident, divers could have been stranded underwater. The divers were selected for their experience and were under the control of diving superintendent Mike O'Meara. It is said that some of the divers received £30,000 for their part in the operation and the risks they took.

The *Stephaniturm* sailed from Peterhead in Scotland on 30 August 1981. On board were representatives from the MOD and Department of Trade, as well as two Soviet officials. The divers had been briefed prior to departing and throughout the sea trip so that by the time they reached the location they knew where the gold should be stored and its position on the vessel. The first dives would be to survey the wreck, and confirm that it was indeed the *Edinburgh*.

Time would be a major factor as the operation was undertaken inside the

Arctic, which is renowned for its rough weather. If the gold was to be found the divers had to determine the exact position of the bomb room. They had one advantage in that a sister ship, HMS *Belfast*, was moored on the River Thames in London where it was preserved as a museum, so the salvors were able to take a close look at that.

While the *Stephaniturm* held station using its dynamic positioning system, divers worked from the diving bell 244 m (800 ft) below in the icy Arctic waters. The wreck made an immediate impression on them, as described by one of the divers in Barrie Penrose's book *Stalin's Gold*: 'I stepped out on the bottom of the bell weight, with the lights on the ship's hull, and really it was just massive . . . And the amazing thing that I noticed after being down for five to ten minutes was that there were no fish, hardly any sea life. And the torpedo hole was big enough for a detached house to fit inside.'

The plan was to cut a hole in the ship and enter the bomb room, remove the gold, recover it to the surface and return home. A straightforward task, until, that is, the divers had cut the hole and were able to look inside and see the tangled mess of debris. It was not going to be an easy or a quick job.

Perhaps the single most important person in the diving team is the diving superintendent, and Mike O'Meara was one of the best and most competent that could have been selected for this operation. Saturation diving is a team effort and those who could compromise the team have to be held together, especially in a job such as this where no gold meant no pay. Peer pressure, risk taking, disappointment and fatigue become very relevant factors, and the diving superintendent has to stand back and not be seen to side with one group or another, but maintain the balance for the good of the overall operation. Mike O'Meara did just that, from day one, until the expedition returned to the UK.

In the murky gloom the divers entered the wreck and began the task of removing the debris and bombs. Their umbilicals, which provided life support from the div-ing bell, snaked into the black hole behind them. While inside, the divers would have been aware that if the ship had not been able to maintain station in an emergency situation they would almost certainly have been killed.

Fear of death would have been far from the mind of the diver who lifted the heavy object and put it close to his helmet face plate so that he could see what it was. His light gave a clue as it shone on it, but the embossed number, KP0620, confirmed it. A gold bar valued at £100,000 had been found. During this dive, another four bars were found and recovered. If morale had been flagging amongst the salvage team, this altered everything. It had taken 13 days to get into the bomb room and recover gold.

The wooden boxes that had held the gold bars crumpled when touched, so each individual bar had to be taken to the outside of the ship and placed in a special basket for recovery to the surface. The salvage operation was in full spate now, with a competition between the divers to see who could recover the most gold bars in one dive. The special recovery cage posed a problem in that it could only recover £4 million worth of gold at one time!

The divers encountered problems that could have jeopardized the entire operation. They were working very hard at extreme depths and this caused fatigue, which increased daily. Some of the divers developed sore ears, not an uncommon experience for saturation divers, but the expedition did not have adequate medical supplies. The water supplied to the divers' hot water suits was often so hot that if it touched bare skin it burned it. Therefore there were divers with burns which never had a chance to heal in the humid atmosphere of the saturation complex, and they were susceptible to further burns. It was perhaps ironic that an expedition that was so remote from medical assistance did not include a doctor.

The divers moved further into the bomb room, clearing debris and recovering gold bars. Eventually the amount of time spent clearing the piles of twisted steel and bombs increased and the recovery of gold very much reduced. The divers were exhausted and there was tons more debris to be moved. The weather had deteriorated with gales and heavy seas, which meant that the cost of continuing the operation outweighed the possible recovery, so on 7 October the operation was terminated and the *Stephaniturm* sailed for Murmansk. Under the supervision of the Russians the 431 gold bars they had recovered were divided. Fifty five per cent went to the Russian and British governments and 45 per cent to the salvors. The remaining gold bars stayed below, awaiting the next expedition . . .

Chapter 5

Testing the Tables

IT WAS DISCOVERED long ago that human beings could descend underwater, but how long they could remain there was limited to the length of time they could hold their breath. Exploiting the underwater world required the intrepid underwater explorers to have a means of breathing. Basic underwater breathing equipment enabled man not only to remain below for longer, but to dive deeper. These two things combined equalled trouble, because of the physiological combination of time, depth and decompression. There are no records of how many early divers fell foul of this problem and perished as a result.

While divers and engineers developed ways and means of working at greater depths, scientists struggled with the fact that if a diver remained at depth for a lengthy period of time, he encountered physical effects when he returned to the surface. One man found the answer and was to place diving research on a sound footing.

In the late 1800s, Paul Bert, the French physiologist, discovered that certain important factors played a crucial role in efforts to put man underwater to deeper depths and for longer periods. He found that when a diver was subjected to pressure at depth, bubbles of nitrogen gas entered his bloodstream and that, to enable them to dissolve safely, the diver needed to return to the surface slowly. He stated: 'For they must not only allow time for the nitrogen of the blood to escape, but also to allow the nitrogen of the tissues time to pass into the blood'. He further found that if a diver came to the surface and developed decompression sickness – the bends – he could be relieved of the pain by being recompressed and then gradually returned to the surface. The introduction of steel recompression chambers made this possible.

At this time there were no decompression tables. If treatment of the bends was successful, it was by luck rather than by judgement. Furthermore, Bert discovered that breathing pure oxygen under pressure created serious problems, but the risks of decompression sickness could be reduced by mixing the oxygen with either nitrogen or hydrogen. Bert's experiments were by no means complete or conclusive and not all cases were treated successfully. But his important discoveries were to provide a basis for future developments in decompression tables and the use of mixed gases for breathing.

Research continued in the ensuing years. The need of the Navy to put divers down deeper for longer periods prompted the setting-up of the First Admiralty Deep Diving Committee in 1905. Its task was to develop a way of allowing divers to go deep wearing standard diving dress and to return to the surface without suffering ill-effects.

The scientific member of the committee was Professor John S. Haldane. Haldane had already carried out research into various problems affecting the diver. He had produced a set of decompression tables, as yet untested, which would enable the diver to go to a depth of 55 m (180 ft). Under the umbrella of this committee, Haldane could at last put his tables to the test.

Haldane's first trials were carried out on goats, chosen because their reactions under pressure are similar to those of the human body. The tests were carried out in steel chambers with heavy sealing doors. Inside, the animals were subjected to air under pressure and then, in the shallow ranges, to oxygen. The tables were proved, modifications completed, and the experimental unit moved to Scotland. Here, volunteer divers undertook dives and subsequent decompression to prove the tables in full operation. Following these tables became the accepted procedure for diving.

As time passed, divers needed to go even deeper, and it was in 1930 that the Second Admiralty Deep Diving Committee was set up with the aim of developing diving tables that would allow air breathing standard divers to go down to 91.5 m (300 ft). Goats were again called into service for the initial experiments. Two decompression chambers were used which allowed the animals to be pressurised to 91.5 m (300 ft) for up to 30 minutes. The goats were then gradually decompressed until they reached 18.3 m (60 ft), at which point the atmosphere in the chambers was changed from air to oxygen to reduce the length of decompression. Twelve goats were used in this series of experiments. However, the tables proved unsuccessful, and a number of animals developed decompression sickness. The results of this first phase were compiled and modified, and another set of tables produced. This time, no less than 85 goats found themselves in the experimental tanks over the following months.

The tables that eventually evolved required stops being made at given depths for fixed periods, and a change in atmosphere to oxygen at the shallower depths. This time, the tables worked. Volunteer divers assumed their role in the programme, to prove them for general human use. By the end of this experimental period, divers had achieved working dives to 97.5 m (320 ft).

Development of deep diving techniques halted after Italian charioteers attacked Allied ships at Gibraltar in 1941. Winston Churchill ordered that the British were to concentrate on forming special underwater units to strike back at the enemy.

That was easier said than done as the Italians had been experimenting with equipment and underwater vehicles over a number of years before the Second World War, while Britain had been focusing on deep diving. There was therefore a lot of catching up for the British to do, and they had neither the equipment nor the trained personnel for shallow covert operations. The Admiralty hastily established a diving committee tasked with organizing operational units.

In response, the committee formed the Experimental Diving Unit, who were to develop oxygen closed-circuit breathing apparatus and appropriate operational procedures for shallow water operations. The Siebe Gorman company already had relevant experience with oxygen breathing equipment, and they were invited to participate by providing expertise as well as allowing their diving facilities at Tolworth to be taken over for research. Professor Haldane was the physiological adviser, and the human guinea-pigs were volunteers for special service. They knew noth-

Animals have always played a vital part in diving research, with the best results being obtained from pigs and goats. The most famous of the animals was a goat, 'Lord Nelson', who undertook numerous experiments during the Second World War with no ill-effects and provided the researchers with vital data. (Royal Navy)

During the Second World War and in the post-war years, research into breathing gas and decompression was carried out by the Royal Navy with commercial support from the Siebe Gorman company. By modern standards the equipment was very primitive, but it sufficed and enabled the researchers and volunteer divers to carry out their vital work. (Royal Navy)

ing of the role they were to play in the tests, but were led in their actions by diving officers and instructors, supported by medical staff and laboratory assistants.

Once more, goats found themselves in the chamber first, 'diving' to various depths in an oxygen atmosphere. Then it was the turn of the men. They worked in pairs in two large decompression chambers. The first man acted as the attendant (breathing air), while the other breathed pure oxygen. Bolted inside the steel chambers, they were compressed to a given depth. Outside, instructors controlled the operation, while medical staff monitored procedures. The human guinea-pigs breathed oxygen and gave a sign when they felt the first sensation of oxygen poisoning, a tingling of the lips. They knew this would be followed by convulsions and then total loss of consciousness. As the diver reached the more dramatic stages, the attendant provided assistance until the chamber could be bled off and the door opened, allowing the medical team access to the unfortunate diver.

More than one thousand dives were undertaken without the loss of a single life, although on occasion it was a pretty close thing. Such was the camaraderie that developed amongst the divers that they

invented a fictitious monster for the chamber which they called 'Oxygen Pete'. The divers competed with one another to see who could fight off the effects of Pete the longest. When they experienced the first effects of oxygen poisoning, the men would move their lips around the mouthpiece to stop the sensation. But they could do nothing when the convulsions came. These experiments showed that oxygen was poisonous below two atmospheres of water. It was also found that divers using oxygen closed-circuit breathing apparatus were limited to an operational depth of 10 m (33 ft). However, in reality, many divers found themselves at greater depths than this, which affected some of them, but not others.

In the final stages of the war, the Admiralty Experimental Diving Unit digressed from researching combat diving and equipment to studying deep diving. Once again, naval divers found themselves working with animals, as they experimented with mixed gases and decompression procedures. When the war ended, experimental work moved away from Tolworth to HMS *Vernon* at Portsmouth. New trials were undertaken to put divers below the 91.5 m (300 ft) barrier using the oxy-helium techniques originally developed by the United States Navy.

A major milestone in deep diving experiments was reached in 1948 when Petty Officer William Bollard RN broke the world record for deep diving when he descended to a depth of 163 m (535 ft). He used the Siebe Gorman standard dress with the specially designed helmet injector device and carbon dioxide absorbent chamber. He also used a helium and oxygen breathing mixture and the Davis Submersible Decompression Chamber (diving bell). Today, the diving bell is placed close to the work site, but during the naval deep dives, the bell was deployed at 58 m (190 ft) and the diver descended from there to the planned depth, his umbilical being tended by personnel on the support vessel. The slow ascent was undertaken by following a pre-placed rope to the bell, where an in-water decompression stop was carried out. He then entered the bell assisted by a tender.

When the inside door was closed, the bell was recovered to the surface and connected to the decompression chambers on the support vessel, where the divers could transfer under pressure. In 1956 Senior Command Boatswain George Wookey RN, wearing the same type of apparatus and diving bell, reached a depth of 183 m (600 ft) off the Norwegian coast.

It was in the late 1960s that Royal Navy divers reached even greater depths. The divers were members of the Deep Trials Unit and carried out experimental work at the Royal Naval Physiological Laboratory at Alverstoke, Portsmouth, England. The Royal Navy did not have the equipment or diving vessel necessary to put the experimental work into practice in the open sea, but the United States Navy did, so they combined their facilities with the Royal Navy's research knowhow and established a joint programme. Royal Navy divers joined their counterparts in the USA and began a programme of deep diving trials that resulted in Chief Petty Officer V. J. Humphrey and Lt R. G. Lusty joining two US Navy divers in an open sea dive to a depth of 350 m (1,148 ft). The record dive was made on 3 June 1975 in the Gulf of Mexico, about 129 km (80 miles) southwest of Panama City. The divers used the Mark 1 Deep Diving System which was installed aboard a US Navy support vessel. The dive team spent a total of 15 days under pressure, of which almost 11 of those days were spent in decompression. This placed deep diving within the grasp of the Royal Navy, but it was not followed up, and it was the commercial diving industry that gained from this research and development.

Deep diving is a strange phenomenon, as being under pressure at depth does not affect people in the same way. Two divers can dive to the same depth for the same period of time and undergo the same decompression profile, but only one of them will develop decompression sickness. This is further exemplified by one of Jacques Cousteau's films in which he followed the exploits of a coral diver in the Mediterranean Sea. The diver used compressed air to dive to 91.5 m (300 ft) in order to recover prized black coral. (In the UK, commercial diving using compressed air is restricted to 50 m (165 ft)). His only support was a woman who could not dive and an inflatable rubber boat. To film the exploits of the coral diver, the French team arrived aboard a diving support vessel equipped with helium and oxygen breathing gas, decompression chambers and qualified personnel to deal with any diving-related problems.

The coral diver entered the water from the rubber boat equipped with compressed air cylinders which were pressurized well above the safe pressure limit. He followed a weighted rope down to the seabed and began to hack away at the coral, placing the pieces in a bag. Cousteau's divers wore full diving equipment, including helmets, and breathed a helium/oxygen gas mix. They were provided with their gas and communications through umbilicals. They filmed the adventurer with professional equipment.

The time spent underwater was judged by the amount of air left in the cylinders, and when the gauge needle reached a certain point (predetermined by the coral diver from past experience) he left the bottom and began a slow ascent towards the surface. At a depth he seemed content with, he stopped on the rope and carried out a 'wet decompression stop'. This is quite normal, but the stop depth would usually be measured accurately, and the time the diver had to remain there would be pre-determined by the time he had spent at the maximum depth. The coral diver had no knowledge of any of these details and merely did what he thought best. The woman in the boat lowered down full compressed air cylinders and recovered the used ones, and in this manner the coral diver undertook his 'decompression'.

When he considered that he had spent enough time in the water, he surfaced, climbed into the boat, and the pair returned to shore. During the filming operation the French divers ran into problems which required some speedy action and treatment in the decompression chamber. This was for a team which had been meticulously controlled throughout the dive. The coral diver was not fit by any stretch of the imagination and no-one could tell how long he would be able to carry on diving. Unfortunately, that will never be known, because he was subsequently killed in an argument over a garden hose.

A Swiss engineer, Hans Keller, developed a gas mixture and diving tables which would allow him to reach depths not previously reached by divers. He needed professional support, and that was provided by the French Navy. In 1960 he successfully completed a simulated dive in a pressure chamber to a depth of 250 m (820 ft). He remained at depth for five seconds before undertaking a controlled decompression to the surface. The US Navy were very interested in Hans Keller's experiments and made available to him their deep diving facilities. In late 1961 he carried out an experimental dive using his own formulated gas mixture, diving and decompression tables to a depth of 213 m (700 ft). His decompression was undertaken in about two-and-a-half hours.

Having had such success with the simulated dives, the next phase required an open water dive and this was undertaken in 1963 off the coast of California. Keller was accompanied by Peter Small, a journalist with the *National Geographical Magazine*. The dive required the use of a

diving bell. The bell was lowered with the two men in an air atmosphere while breathing a helium and oxygen mixture from masks. At a depth of 305 m (1,000 ft) the bell was stopped and pressurized internally to a depth equal to that outside. Keller then left the bell, having only just enough time (air) to plant the Swiss and US flags on the seabed.

At this point the dive began to go wrong. The Swiss flag was so large that he became entangled in it and this delayed his return to the bell. In fact he ran out of breathing gas and only made it back to the bell by holding his breath. In his rush to get back into the bell and seal the door so that the ascent could begin, a fin caught in the seating of the door and it was not closed when the bell was recovered. This had catastrophic results because no decompression table was followed. When the bell reached 61 m (200 ft) it was stopped and two divers were deployed from the support vessel to investigate the situation. They reported that both men were unconscious and the decision was made to recover the bell to the surface. Adding to the growing disaster, one of the investigating divers was swept away and never seen again. On the surface, the bell door was opened and both men removed. Keller was unconscious but survived the ordeal; Small had suffered an explosive decompression and had died during the recovery of the bell. Keller had proved his theory in practice but not as a safe system of working.

By the 1970s, companies involved in offshore oil exploration had moved their operations into deeper water, and they needed diving support services to be able to operate there. This meant that diving contractors had to invest in deep diving systems which could sustain divers under pressure for weeks at a time. More importantly, they had to develop reliable and safe diving and decompression tables. The US Navy had a well-proven set of tables, but the commercial operators wanted to put divers deeper for longer and decompress them back to the surface quicker. The only way to develop the tables was to undertake controlled experiments in specialist hyperbaric chamber facilities, under

Hans Keller, the Swiss engineer, developed a helium and oxygen breathing mixture and decompression tables which would allow him to dive to 305 m (1,000 ft). He proved his theory, but the dive had catastrophic consequences. (US Navy)

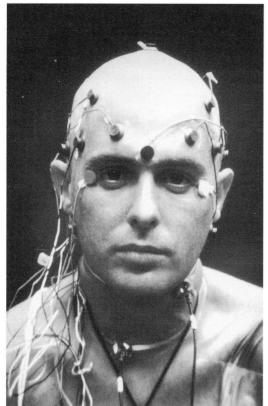

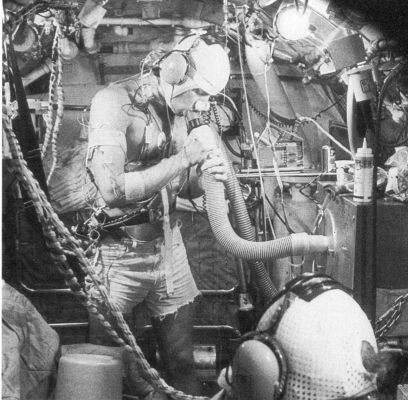

the control of scientists and medical experts.

Two of the world's largest diving contractors at that time were Oceaneering International of the USA and Comex of France. Both companies had contracts throughout the world, often in remote locations where help would be limited, so the diving tables and associated treatment tables had to work, and that took time, money, research and volunteer divers.

Comex established its hyperbaric facilities at Marseilles in France in 1964 and based them upon the EMS 600 chamber complex. The modular complex of chambers was designed to simulate human dry and wet dives to depths up to 700 m (2,296 ft). The complex is comprised of three interconnecting steel spheres, each 2.5 m (8.2 ft) in diameter. One is a living chamber in which divers spend the non-working periods of the dive, the second is the changing and sanitary unit, and that affords access to the third chamber, which is described as the 'wet' chamber. It is situated below the second chamber, and can be filled with water. This allows the divers to carry out experiments or work projects

under controlled conditions. Because of the world-wide nature of the operations undertaken by Comex, their divers need to undertake experimental dives in extreme conditions. To meet these requirements the water temperature in the complex can be lowered to –2° C to simulate dives in Arctic conditions.

The EMS 600 chamber complex is surrounded with controls and command consoles to provide facilities for research workers, doctors, physiologists, chemists, psychologists, ergonomists and technical specialists. They can prepare the divers for a range of tasks and monitor the output, which when evaluated provides vital data for the preparation of commercially acceptable procedures.

In 1970 Comex constructed the hydrosphere, which is a large chamber where the lower half can be filled with water and pressurized to a depth of 300 m (984 ft). The design of the system allowed for work sites to be placed inside, for divers to test their own abilities and that of special tools. It was in the hydrosphere that Comex carried out its hyperbaric welding research. In its complex, Comex divers

An Oceaneering diver is wired up with monitoring equipment as part of a deep diving research programme which was undertaken when diving in 1974–5 at a US university. (Oceaneering International)

Inside the test chamber the volunteers had to live amongst a wide variety of equipment that monitored them while working and at rest. The main aim of research during the 1970s was to determine how deep divers could go and what functions they could undertake. Research into breathing gases was undertaken, and the effect of pressure on body and brain was also monitored. (Oceaneering)

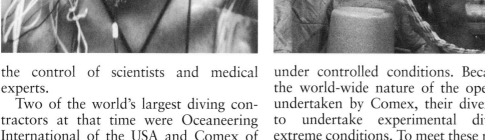

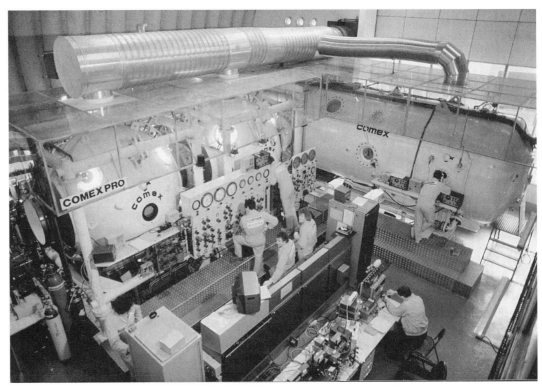

Without doubt, the world leader in the development of diving tables and deep diving research has been Comex. The Hyperbaric Experimental Centre was established in 1963, before the petroleum industry had begun to look at exploiting resources in deeper water. As technology improved, equipment was replaced and more facilities made available to the scientists and technicians who controlled and prepared research information on various projects. Today, the EMS 600 complex allows divers to simulate dives to 7,000 m (22,367 ft). (Comex)

carried out a simulated dive to 610 m (2,001 ft) in 1972. They also carried out an experiment which combined simulated dives and dives in the open sea. The series was known as the 'Janus' series and the final dive took place in 1977 off Cavalaire, in the South of France, where six divers worked at 460 m (1,509 ft) and two divers worked at 501 m (1,643 ft). In the 'Entex 9' dive of 1983, divers spent 40 days under pressure, with 14 days at 450 m (1,476 ft) and 610 m (2,001 ft). During this operation 20 wet dives were undertaken at depths of 450 m, 520 m (1,706 ft) and 610 m.

Drager, a German company that is synonymous with deep diving equipment, has the GUSI Diving Simulator which allows wet and dry diving operations to be carried out to a simulated water depth of 671 m (2,200 ft). The system allows divers to transfer through an internal lock from a dry chamber to the 'wet' chamber. The divers can also be transferred by using a diving bell which can be locked on to the top of the wet chamber, which will allow divers to copy operational conditions. The large wet chamber can be opened to its full diameter to allow large items of equipment to be placed inside, where they

can be subjected to pressure tests.

In Aberdeen, Scotland, the National Hyperbaric Centre is dedicated to research. The hub of the system is a 16-man saturation diving system with a depth capability of 600 m (1,968 ft) connected to a large hydrostatic chamber. This chamber can emulate wet or dry sub-sea depths of 1,000 m (3,281 ft) or altitudes of 50,000 m (164,050 ft). The centre also provides a hyperbaric lifeboat reception facility where divers who have been evacuated from a saturation diving complex offshore can be transported in the lifeboat and transferred under pressure into the chamber complex.

In addition, the centre provides support for the Transfer Under Pressure (TUP) system which comprises a small helicopter-transportable compression chamber which allows sick or injured divers to be transferred under pressure from an operational saturation system to the centre where they can be given medical treatment while remaining under pressure. As well as offering a capability for full-scale trials for both manual and mechanical hyperbaric welding, it is a centre of excellence for research and development in sub-sea technologies and the study of human per-

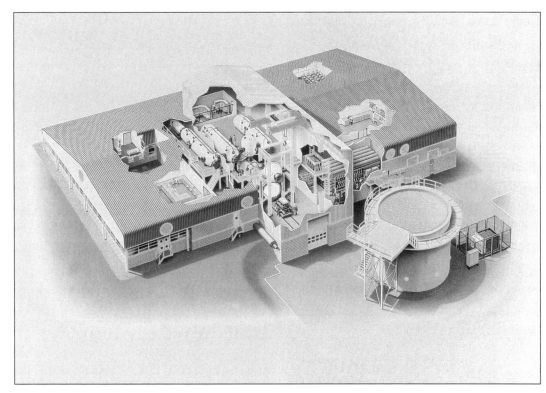

A drawing of the National Hyperbaric Centre in Aberdeen, Scotland. A range of pressure chambers allow a wide variety of research and training projects to be undertaken, and equipment designed to operate underwater can be tested and tried out. (National Hyperbaric Centre)

formance. Excellent research facilities for deep diving trials are also still much in evidence, both in Scotland and in France.

The hyperbaric complexes have played a major part in the development of diving tables and their corresponding decompression profiles for many years, and they continue to do so. They have also enabled detailed and controlled research to be carried out with deep diving breathing gas mixtures. Since 1977 Comex have been investigating developing new breathing mixtures which would allow divers to go beyond 610 m (2,001 ft). Deep diving using helium and oxygen gas mixtures is well established, but Comex discovered

The Diver Rescue Transfer-Under-Pressure System was designed to provide a method of transfer for an injured diver or group of divers, under pressure, from an offshore diving system to a hyperbaric chamber complex at the National Hyperbaric Centre in Aberdeen. The basic system comprises a transfer chamber (shown on top) and a helicopter chamber. The transfer chamber can hold one injured diver, or possibly two divers in an extreme emergency, and can be moved by seven men using handles, a trolley, or a ship's or installation's crane. The helicopter chamber can hold an injured diver plus one or two attendants, and in extreme emergency conditions it can accommodate up to eight divers. This chamber remains in the helicopter and the divers are transferred to it under pressure from the transfer chamber. (National Hyperbaric Centre)

The helicopter chamber is fitted inside a helicopter, where it remains throughout the offshore phase of the rescue. When the helicopter has landed ashore, the chamber with the divers inside is removed and transported to the Hyperbaric Centre, where it is connected to a large chamber, allowing the divers to transfer through. An injured diver can then receive medical treatment while remaining under pressure. (National Hyperbaric Centre)

gen, but he had discovered that, while perfect for respiration, a gas mixture using hydrogen could be liable to explode unless the correct percentages were strictly maintained for different water depths. Hydrogen is twice as light as helium, and costs considerably less. It was considered a viable alternative to helium, either in the form of a hydrogen and oxygen mixture or, to reduce the explosive potential, the two parts could include helium as a third gas. Comex considered the possibility of using a hydrogen mix to enable divers to reach 1,000 m (3,281 ft). Research will continue to explore potential gas mixtures and the development of diving tables to reach and return from deep dives.

In spite of the rapid advances being made in underwater robotics, the ability to operate in deeper water means that there is a need for divers to be able to dive deeper. The balance of evidence at present shows that some tasks are not suited to robots or atmospheric diving suits but require human intervention. Therefore divers need to be able to reach even deeper depths, but they must be able to do so effectively and, even more importantly, the dive must be safe in all aspects. This means that research will need to continue.

In April and May 1993 'Aura 93', a simulated saturation diving programme to 450 and 470 m (1,476 and 1,542 ft), was undertaken at the National Hyperbaric Centre in Aberdeen, Scotland. The team comprised four divers, two British and two French, who were pressurized in the saturation system to a holding depth of 450 m. The divers remained at the holding depth for seven days and made two excursions to 470 m.

A research project of this kind has to have a programme of objectives, and they will involve equipment, in-water experiments and those which involve monitoring in the dry. For the divers' equipment, they tested three different systems of underwater breathing apparatus (UBAs). They were the Comex PRO BOS Mk II, DIVEX SLS Mk III and the OBS UBA 90-400, and were worn during the 'wet' dives. The divers also tested and evaluated a range of hot water suits and communication systems. Linked into the helmet

that beyond the 300 m (984 ft) depth heliox may not completely remove High Pressure Nervous Syndrome (HPNS), which was observed, described and named for the first time at Comex's hyperbaric unit in 1968.

Peter Bennett, an American, originated the use of Trimix, which comprised helium, oxygen and nitrogen, and in 1981 three divers reached a depth of 686 m (2,250 ft) in a simulated chamber dive. The density of nitrogen in Trimix is seven times that of helium and it is therefore not a suitable gas for deep diving. The ideal solution was, in theory, a mixture of hydrogen and oxygen.

It was the American physicist and chemist Elihu Thompson who first proposed the breathing of hydrogen and oxy-

system were bail-out bottles, containing the emergency breathing gas supply carried by all divers. They were tested for duration at depth with different breathing rates. As in all deep trials, the divers were medically monitored with ultrasound monitoring, and this was not complicated by the use of new or experimental gas mixes. The tasks which the divers carried out included Magnetic Particle Inspection (MPI), wet welding and pipework construction. During the decompression phase, the divers carried out a lost bell survival trial which involves specialist equipment. This again confirmed that an emergency is a test of the divers as well as the equipment.

Divers will continue to dive deeper, both for research purposes and in operations, but for the foreseeable future the depths will be restricted to those undertaken in the National Hyperbaric Centre 'Aura 93' project and Comex's ongoing deep diving programmes.

Research into divers' health and new diving tables is undertaken in controlled conditions in hyperbaric facilities. The diver exercises inside the chamber while staff on the outside monitor him. (National Hyperbaric Centre)

Chapter 6

Underwater Habitats

DEEP UNDERWATER EXPLORATION by men and machine was for a long time the preserve of the military and the offshore oil and gas industry. Both had the financial resources to fund research and development, particularly into the possibility of divers diving deeper and for longer periods. Scientists, on the other hand, who were also interested in deep diving because they wanted to explore the deep oceans and investigate the varied marine life there, had to procure funding and that was not easy. Fish farming, kelp cultivation and the study of undersea flora and fauna were among a long list of research projects which oceanographic bodies needed to study, but they did not have the same influence as defence or the commercial exploitation of petrochemicals. Funding was available commercially for research into the physical effects of saturation diving and breathing mixed gases, because industry required deep diving for specific work tasks.

Deep diving saturation systems were designed, built and placed aboard the rigs or diving support vessels. It was a very expensive business, and the returns had to warrant the investment. The methods of saturation diving used by commercial divers and underwater scientists were completely different, for the former maintained their divers in chamber complexes on the vessels or rigs, while the institutions wanted their scientists to remain in the complexes, underwater. This meant that the non-commercial institutions that gained funding for research had to develop ways of keeping those who were to undertake the work under pressure.

Scientific underwater research projects required scientists to live and work at depth, and this required the development of underwater laboratories, or, as they were more commonly known, habitats. These habitats were placed on the seabed with the aid of divers working from surface support vessels. Once in place the researchers, who were either already inside the habitat or free-dived from the surface to enter the system, would begin their research programmes. Their bodies would then become saturated with gas and even though the early habitats were only in 15 m (50 ft) of water depth, the researchers could only return to the surface after undergoing decompression.

During the late 1960s and early '70s a number of institutions co-operated with underwater system manufacturers to design and develop habitats. The technology existed in the form of submarines, but they worked on the principle of keeping the occupants at atmospheric pressure rather than allowing them to be at an equivalent depth. The systems that were developed operated for the most part in shallow water, but systems that would carry research into deeper water required more enhanced designs to withstand the greater pressure.

The first practical open sea demonstrations were undertaken in 1962 with the 'Man-in-Sea One' programme of E. A. Link (one man breathing helium–oxygen at 61 m (200 ft) for 24 hours), and 'Conshelf One' of Captain Jacques-Yves Cousteau (six men breathing a nitrogen and oxygen mixture at 10 m (35 ft) for 7 days). These pioneers extended both depth and duration during 1964. In that year Link and Lamberstsen conducted a two-day exposure of two men at 131 m (430 ft), and Cousteau's 'Conshelf Two' experiment maintained a group of seven men for 30 days at 11 m (36 ft) and 27 m (90 ft) with excursion dives to much greater depths.

The best-known US Navy experimental effort in saturation diving is the Sealab programme. It was in Sealab I, under the direction of Captain Bond, that four men remained underwater for a total of 11 days in 1964 at an average depth of 59 m (193 ft). A year later, Sealab II put three teams of 10 men each in a habitat at 62 m (205 ft). Each team spent 15 days at depth, and one man remained for 30 days. Later experiments have taken divers to 11.5 m (38 ft) for two months (Tektite I (1969), conducted under the joint sponsorship of the US Navy, Department of Interior, and NASA), and 158.5 m (520 ft) for five days in 1970.

As a result of these experiments and research projects, two basic concepts of saturation diving technique have evolved. In one, the divers actually live underwater for the duration of the dive and are supported in a large submerged habitat. The habitat contains appropriate systems for diver safety and comfort. The habitat is not normally a pressure chamber, so some arrangement must be made for appropriate decompression at the end of the operation. In the other saturation diving technique, the divers are transported in a diving bell between the underwater work site and a surface chamber, where they are maintained in saturated conditions, but in more comfortable (and less hazardous) living conditions than in a habitat.

One of the most productive underwater laboratories was Hydro Lab. It was the longest-running operation ever and began in the late 1960s; by the end of 1975 more than 200 people had undertaken saturation projects in it, including 22 women. The habitat was 4.87 m (16 ft) in length and 2.42 m (8 ft) in diameter, and within

Sealab II is lowered into place while team members check the outside. Sealab experiments involved teams of four scientists being committed to the laboratory, underwater, for periods of up to 14 days. (US Navy)

these confines three to four people could be accommodated for a period of up to a week at a time. Facilities were very basic and included bunks, table, chairs, a shower and a toilet. The life support system installed in the facility included a carbon dioxide removal system and dehumidifiers. For diver excursions to undertake research projects the divers left and entered the habitat through a trunk. Because their bodies were 'saturated' throughout the entire operation, the divers could not return to the surface directly without undergoing a decompression profile.

As was to be the case with all of the underwater laboratories, Hydro Lab required a surface support vessel that could remain on station throughout the period that researchers were underwater. The life support system on the support vessel was designed to operate unmanned and without the need for resupply or maintenance. It provided a generator to power the lights and life support system in the habitat, water tanks to provide a supply of fresh water, and pre-mixed gas mixtures to make up the habitat's atmosphere, to maintain the correct breathing mixture. The emergency system was designed to provide life support for the occupants for the duration of the decompression profile. A radio link was established between the habitat and the support vessel where it was transmitted to the onshore research station. This would be the only contact the underwater researchers had with those on the surface. All of the surface support facilities were supplied through an umbilical, though if that was severed, the habitat did carry its own limited life support facilities.

Among those who participated in research projects were Senator Lowell Weicker of Connecticut, Congressman Bill Alexander of Arkansas and Howard W. Pollock, Deputy Administrator of the National Oceanic and Atmospheric Administration. They lived and worked in and around the habitat and took part in underwater research projects. The site was on a sand and coral bottom adjacent to a reef and offered an ideal location for examining the flora and fauna. Upon completion of their programme they required decompression of $13^{1}/2$ hours in order to return to surface atmosphere.

The range of experiments conducted from Hydro Lab involved fish farming, reef fauna, marine life and the cultivation of kelp. Studies were also done of the teams, who spent periods of up to seven days in saturation. When conducting their experiments, they had the use of submersible craft for operational evaluation and test purposes. One team carried out specialist research into the physical aspects of being in saturation.

Throughout 1971, Hydro Lab was used to support a series of experiments and research projects that involved the study of sediments, currents, acoustics, pollutants and the development and testing of underwater instrumentation. By mid-1972, 368 persons had operated in the habitat, adding up a total of some 5,544 man hours, and by the end of 1974, Hydro Lab had been used for 21 underwater scientific projects with 101 researchers being maintained at depth in saturation for a total of 613 man days.

A laboratory with a similar operation to that of Hydro Lab was the La Chalupa, which was designed and built for the Marine Resources Department Foundation of Puerto Rico. One of the most revolutionary aspects of this design was that the laboratory had four hydraulically operated legs. Once the laboratory had been submerged it rested on its legs and could be jacked to a level plane by using the hydraulic system. The operation of the laboratory was the same as others of the period but it did have an advantage in that it had a submarine garage built into it that allowed small submersibles to be used to aid the divers on their research projects.

One of the better-known underwater habitats or laboratories was Tektite I. It was designed and developed in 1969 to support a series of underwater scientific studies that included 'in water' and 'in habitat' projects. The results of these studies would provide valuable information to their numerous sponsors, who included the US National Science Foundation, the US Navy, NASA and the US Department of Interior.

The Tektite habitat comprised two vertical pressure chambers, each of which was divided into two compartments, providing upper and lower rooms. In one of the chambers, the upper room served as the control room where the habitat's communication and life support controls were maintained. This room was vital in that it offered the only communications link to the surface support craft. The lower compartment of this cylinder provided the living accommodation where the team members spent their off-duty time, and contained bunks and a galley. The upper room of the other chamber housed the essential air purification and air conditioning systems. A tunnel 1.37 m (4 ft 4 in) in diameter linked the two upper rooms, allowing the occupants free access to all parts of the habitat. The lower compartment of the second cylinder was the divers' work area and contained the entry and exit trunk through which members of the team could enter the water when conducting 'in water' diving operations. Each compartment also had portholes that allowed the researchers a restricted view of the water that surrounded them. A cupola located on the top of one of the cylinders had a series of portholes gave those inside a 360° viewing range.

Tektite required a surface support vessel to provide gas, water and electricity and maintain a communication link. The experiments could continue as long as the surface vessel could remain on station, but in the event of bad weather the occupants below were reliant upon emergency systems. Although the habitat was established in water depths of only 15 m (50 ft), those inside were saturated in a gas mixture of nitrogen and oxygen. This meant that all occupants had to undergo a lengthy period of decompression before they could return to the surface.

The success of Tektite I prompted the sponsors to provide an uprated version, in the form of Tektite II. The new habitat could house a team of five and supported ten saturation research projects during its working life. One study was very relevant as it reviewed the physical and mental effects of maintaining a team in saturation for 60 days.

While the USA was at the forefront of underwater habitat development and experiments, the PP Shirshor Institute of Oceanology in the USSR developed the Chernomor 1 in 1969 and followed it with an uprated Mk 2 version. The original Chernomor habitat was used for a number of projects, one of which supported four scientists in saturation for 14 days at a depth of 25 m (82 ft).

Chernomor 2 provided the facility for research experiments at a depth of 30 m (100 ft). Because of the depth at which operations were to be conducted, the habitat was designed to be self-sufficient throughout the deeper operations. This meant that the overall size of the habitat was increased to include storage for breathing gas, fresh water and the regenerating system. The original plan was to carry a self-supporting electrical power supply, but because the duration of the submerged dives was 15 days, no batteries with sufficient power resources were available.

Chernomor 2 began life in 1974 as a joint Soviet and Bulgarian experiment. The site chosen for the first experiment was in the Black Sea at Burgas, off Cape Maslen Nos. The steel chamber was 8 m (26.5 ft) in length and 2.9 m (9.5 ft) in diameter and was sub-divided into three compartments, making a living area, a sanitary area and a diving compartment. Each area was separated by a series of watertight doors that would offer a safe refuge to those working inside in the event of an emergency.

Located on the outside of the main chamber were the life support facilities, comprising fresh water tanks, gas bottle and batteries. There were also ballast tanks that allowed the entire habitat to be floated into place. A regeneration system incorporated a lime chemical absorbent with an active life of seven days, and a supply of new absorption cartridges was carried to allow for up to three weeks' endurance. While it would have been ideal to have been totally self-supporting, as explained above the power supply for lights and the life support system could not be provided from batteries and so a power supply cable was laid from the shore base to the habitat. A second cable provided the communications link between those in the habitat and those ashore.

United States agencies continued with experiments and developments by moving into deeper water. It was in the Pacific Ocean, in 1975, that researchers were saturated in the Aegir habitat for 17 days to undertake a dry dive to a depth of 177 m (580 ft). The project was carried out under the auspices of the University of Hawaii, the developers of the Aegir habitat. Like the Soviet system, it was designed so that the gas mix of helium and oxygen was carried outside the habitat. Fresh water was also carried and, as with the Soviet system, electrical power was supplied through an umbilical from either a surface vessel or shore supply, depending upon weather conditions.

All of these habitat programmes required expensive hardware and life support facilities to enable them to withstand the rigours of being underwater. They also required surface support vessels or support from facilities on land, for throughout the period of the experiments, while the researchers remained at depth, they were exposed to very high risks. Because of the need to maintain the surface support, the number of suitable locations with excellent weather conditions was very limited, and they did not always offer the best research surroundings.

Costs balanced against returns, together with the associated risks, had an impact upon the use of manned seabed habitats. Developers turned their attention to manned submersibles with diver lock-out facilities and saturation diving systems on surface vessels. These made undersea work more cost-effective, efficient, safe and flexible, which resulted in a downturn in the use of seabed habitats for long-term research and has pushed the prospect of man living totally under the sea much further into the future.

Chapter 7

Deep Water Research Vehicles

AN AMERICAN NAMED Bushnell had strong links with the development of submarines and has the honour of having built the first operational military submarine. The *Turtle* was built in 1776 of wood and took an egg-shaped form. It carried a single operator who had to undertake manual functions to control and propel the craft.

To submerge the boat, the operator used a foot-operated valve in the bottom of the boat which allowed water to enter a tank, causing the boat to sink. The volume of water that was allowed to enter determined the depth to which the boat descended. In order to surface, two brass hand-operated force pumps ejected the water, creating buoyancy and so causing the boat to rise. Propulsion and steering were provided by horizontal and vertical screws and a rudder. These were operated by a system of cranks which meant that the operator had to turn handles in order to generate movement and direction. The operator had a gauge which showed the depth of the boat when under the water and a compass which showed the course.

Turtle was designed for warfare and carried an underwater explosive charge. While the boat never achieved the aim of sinking an enemy warship, the principles of submarine operations were proved and have remained the same throughout history. It is technology and materials which have evolved to allow the further exploration of the deep oceans. A hundred and sixty one years elapsed between Bushnell's endeavours and Professor Auguste Piccard's deep ocean research bathyscaphe.

It was in 1937 that Piccard designed the bathyscaphe (mobile bathysphere) and gave it the title *FNRS 2*. The hub of the vessel was a thick wall of steel which was suspended below a container of petrol (gasoline) holding 31,822 l (7,000 gal). The buoyancy container, which was filled with petrol because it is lighter than water, was used to support the sphere, motors, batteries and other equipment. Ballast was carried in the form of lead shot and it could be released by the occupants, allowing the bathyscaphe to rise to the surface. It carried a crew of two who had two 12.7 cm (5 in) view ports through which to carry out observations.

The first dive was made on 24 October 1948 but the bathyscaphe only reached 18 m (60 ft) when it sustained damage and the dive was stopped. A decision was

Dr William Beebe, a naturalist, had developed a fascination for exploring the ocean depths. He worked with Otis Barton to construct the bathysphere in which, in 1934, they reached a depth of 765 m (2,510 ft). The photograph shows Dr Beebe entering the bathysphere in preparation for a dive. (US Navy)

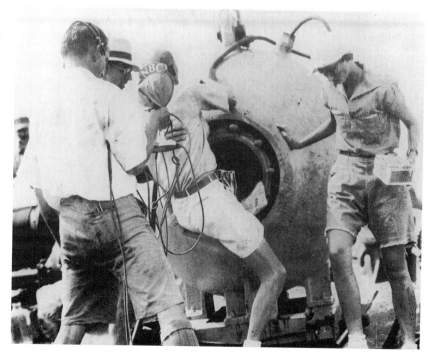

made that for future and deeper dives the bathyscaphe would be unmanned until the system was proved. During the unmanned trials it reached a depth of 1,220 m (4,000 ft). With the success of *FNRS 2* it was decided to build a second craft which could go to greater depths, and in February 1954 the *FNRS 3* carried the operators Houot and Willm to a depth in excess of 3.219 km (2 miles).

After that deep experimental dive Piccard took his expertise to the USA where a new bathyscaphe was built and named *Trieste*. It was launched on 1 August 1953 and after functional and operational trials, a dive was made on 30 September when a depth of 2,880 m (9,450 ft) was reached. *Trieste* continued to undertake research dives until it reached the ultimate depth of 10,668 m (35,800 ft) in the Marianas Trench in 1960. After this dive *Trieste* was restricted to a diving depth of 3,657 m (12,000 ft). Apart from research projects it was used in 1963 to search for the stricken US Navy

nuclear-powered submarine *Thresher*, which had been reported missing in an area south of Newfoundland in a water depth of 2,590 m (8,500 ft). Fitted with sonar, underwater television, magnetometer, radiation detector and photographic equipment, *Trieste* returned from a dive with the vital information which allowed the authorities to determine the cause of the accident. In 1963 the *Trieste* was rebuilt and renamed *Trieste II*, after which it was used in the training of deep submergence vehicle operators. Both Bushnell's and Piccard's exploits caused them to venture into the unknown, and pave the way for vehicles to be developed in order that man could explore underwater.

On land we have developed a variety of highly sophisticated vehicles to transport us and aid our lifestyle. These vehicles have been under constant development since the invention of the wheel and range from a hand cart to a spacecraft. In a much shorter period of time we have developed a range of undersea vehicles

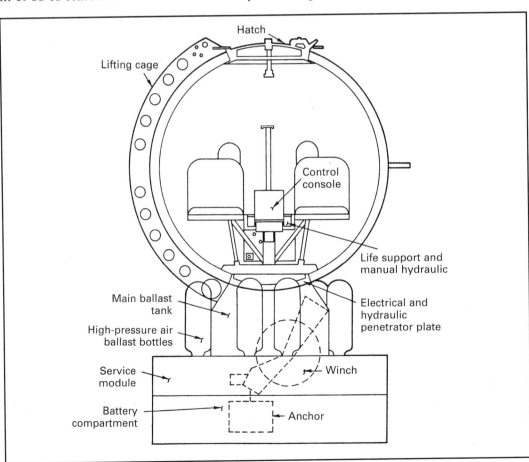

Figure 5: *The* Nemo *submersible.* (Office of the Oceanographer, US Navy)

that are almost as diverse in appearance and application as their counterparts on land.

One of the most unusual undersea vehicles to be developed was the Naval Experimental Manned Observatory (*NEMO*). It was the first underwater vehicle to utilize acrylic plastic for its hull structure. Designed and developed at the Naval Civil Engineering Laboratory, Port Hueneme, California, it was certified in 1970 for operation to depths of 182 m (600 ft).

The unusual design concept provided a panoramic view for the pilot and observer who sat in the atmospheric pressure of the clear sphere. Being untethered, it was completely self-contained and was used for observation and inspection work. It had a major advantage over other submersibles which only had small view ports to look through. A powerful hand-held light was carried and could be shone from the inside of the vehicle to the outside; it also enabled photographs to be taken. For the recovery of samples, a manipulator could be fitted, as could additional lighting and television cameras.

The spherical acrylic plastic pressure hull was surrounded by a structural cage

Left *A scientist and a diver help with the recovery of* NEMO *after a test dive. A conventional crane is used for the lift, which would work in calm water conditions, but not if there was a swell and vessel movement.* (US Navy)

Below *The Perry submersible* Shelf Diver *awaits the order to dive. The vessel was used to support* NEMO *as a safety measure. This picture shows the possible dangers of having the main hatch open whilst on the surface.* (US Navy)

NEMO *undergoing maintenance prior to a dive. The entrance hatch can be seen at the top of the sphere. The flexible hose will provide a flow of fresh air to cleanse the atmosphere inside and keep it cool.* (US Navy)

Figure 6: *The* Makakai *submersible.* (Office of the Oceanographer, US Navy)

tained the main ballast tank, main battery pack and oxygen cylinders. Propulsion was provided by two motors which could move the vehicle at a maximum speed of .75 knots for periods of up to 8 hours. It was not a vehicle designed for a great deal of movement or speed, but for its observation capabilities. The life support system would allow 8 hours' normal operations, but an emergency supply of 24 hours' endurance was also carried.

Inside the sphere, the pilot and observer had an oxygen supply which involved the use of a unit to remove carbon dioxide from exhaled breath. A fan caused air to be drawn into the unit where oxygen was added to it; it was then recirculated around the sphere, ensuring a safe environment. A silica gel and ice combination maintained the humidity. The pilot and observer also each had a closed-circuit rebreather in case of emergency.

NEMO was an experimental craft paid for with military funding, so the results of its research will be diverse, but one result is evident: acrylic plastic can safely be used in large quantities in deep sea submergence vehicles.

Certified in 1972, the *Makakai* also used a clear acrylic plastic sphere. It carried a pilot and observer to a depth of 180 m (600 ft) and had the advantage of being

that carried the entire weight of the *NEMO* system, and was part of the lifting device. It also protected the acrylic plastic hull from impact damage, a critical consideration for this type of vehicle. Beneath the hull was the services unit, which con-

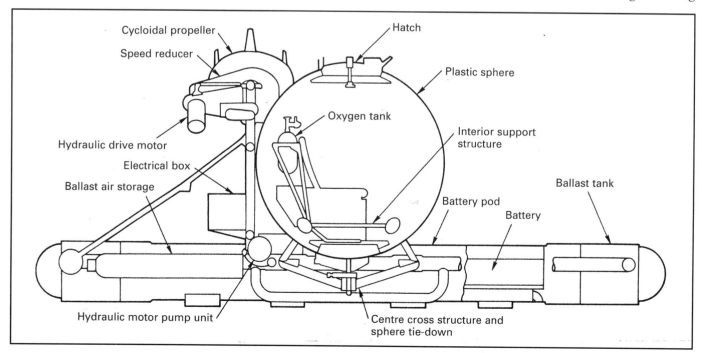

The Makakai *was a more manoeuvrable version of the* NEMO. *The acrylic sphere carried two operators and was mounted on a frame, to which all of the services were fitted. The batteries and buoyancy tanks were located in the cylinder tubes. The new cycloidal propellers, each of which had four short variable pitch blades, can be seen at the rear of the sphere. The craft could be moved in any direction merely by altering the pitch of the propeller.* (US Navy)

designed to be more manoeuvrable than *NEMO*. It provided total panoramic visibility – a great advantage to those studying the seabed and marine life.

The craft was propelled by a unique system of two sets of oppositely arranged thrusters. Each had four short variable pitch propeller blades which enabled the craft to move in any direction merely by altering the pitch of the blades.

Most of the craft's functional systems were located outside the main control sphere in order that the overall size could be kept as small as possible. This was done in order to reduce the heat within the plastic sphere because it had been found that with changing thermal conditions within the craft while submerged, the surface of the sphere fogged over. By reducing the heat, the fogging was reduced. Another reason for placing the control systems outside the sphere was that it allowed for more room inside, and limited the number of penetrators that had to pass through the hull.

The British underwater engineering company OSEL substantially completed the development and construction of

Hawk, a manned vehicle capable of operating at 17,373 m (57,000 ft) with a pressure hull that was to consist of two acrylic hemispheres. Unfortunately it became evident that the vehicle, though technically possible, would not be commercially viable and the development stopped.

The more conventional submersibles were constructed of steel with small view ports fitted at critical locations. These afforded the pilot a restricted view of the world outside so that he could see where he was, and where he was going. These small view ports were also the only means available to the scientists to see what they had come to see. No doubt, until the development of small colour television cameras which could be fitted to the outside and relay pictures to the inside, there were many heated debates as to who should have the view port position, the pilot or the scientist.

Sharing a view port was not a problem for the crew of *Star I*, which was an early experimental craft with limited depth capability. It was a one-man system, with the operator located inside a small steel sphere with very limited observation to

Star I, *an early tear-shaped experimental submersible which carried a single operator. Its two view ports provided limited visibility. The thrusters located either side of the vehicle rotated, giving propulsion in all directions. The vehicle shown is not equipped with any tools and would have been used for observation only. The small wheels located on the underside were used to move the vehicle when on the deck of the surface support vessel.* (US Navy)

the outside. The tear-drop shape was the basis of the design and provided streamlining as well as the buoyancy system. The batteries and life support systems were located within the after section. An uprated vehicle, *Star II*, was built in 1966 and was equipped with a mechanical arm, camera and strobe system; it had an operational depth capability of 366 m (1,200 ft).

Deeper depths, longer duration and more crew members to undertake a greater workload became the criteria for deep sea exploration. In most cases the military were at the forefront of development as they required vehicles that could place and recover seabed sonar listening beacons. There was also a need to salvage military aircraft and weapon systems from the sea in order to obtain vital information.

One of the new generation of submersibles was *Deepstar 4000*, which was capable of operating at 1,200 m (4,000 ft). Its overall design was based upon a saucer concept with a pressure sphere encapsulated within it. The pilot lay in a prone position with a single view port which allowed forward vision so that he

could fly the craft. Also inside the pressure hull were two observers who had limited vision to the outside through other view ports. They did have television camera systems mounted on the front of the vehicle which could be panned and tilted, so they were able to see and record their observations.

Batteries, motors, oxygen and pumps were contained in separate sealed units, giving life support for 48 hours plus an emergency breathing supply. Two horizontal propulsion units, one either side of the craft, provided a speed of 3 knots and an endurance of eight hours. Manoeuvring the craft was achieved by altering the power to either thruster. Going forward on one and reverse on the other would turn the vehicle in place. A range of equipment could be fitted depending on the task to be carried out. Filming was done with 16 mm cine cameras and 70 mm stills cameras. A mechanical arm and claw assembly enabled samples to be gathered and other basic manipulating operations to be undertaken.

Submersibles dive safe in the knowledge that a surface support vessel awaits their return from the depths. However, things do not always go according to plan, as when the *Deepstar 4000* was caught in an underwater current that swept the submersible away from its intended location. As a result, through-water communications between the surface vessel and the submersible were lost. Procedures for such an eventuality are laid down and the *Deepstar*'s crew surfaced the craft. They attempted to make contact using a small CB radio, but due to an electrical storm this was not possible and so eventually the pilot fired flares. The result was that six hours after surfacing they were located and recovered by the support vessel.

Deepstar 4000 was diving off the Mexican coast when it encountered underwater currents. At this time the submersible was moving up a slope from a depth of 1,220 m (4,026 ft). Upon reaching 427 m (1,400 ft) the vehicle was subjected to a second current which increased in speed so that at a depth 274.5 m (900 ft) it reached 2 knots. Added to this problem was the fact that the strong current stirred up the sediment so that the pilot had no visibility. Unable to control the submersible, the pilot was forced to take the craft to the surface, proving yet again the power of the sea over those who venture on and under it.

The sea is not responsible for all incidents. On one occasion *Deepstar 4000* was undertaking a research dive for the US Navy and had just begun its work on the ocean floor when three shells landed and exploded some 183 m (600 ft) astern of the support ship. Urgent radio transmissions were made to stop the firing and the submersible was ordered to the surface. Investigations revealed that the area was designated as a naval exercise zone and the warship had mistaken the support ship for the target ship.

One of the better-known vehicles is the Deep Submergence Research Vehicle *Alvin*, which was delivered to the Woods Hole Oceanographic Institution in 1964. The crew of three could be carried to a depth of 4,000 m (13,120 ft) for periods of up to 72 hours, operating remote from the mother ship on the surface.

Of the vast number of research dives undertaken by *Alvin*, one of the most vital

was the recovery of a hydrogen bomb. Two aircraft, one a USAF bomber, collided in mid-air off the Spanish coast, spreading wreckage, including a payload of hydrogen bombs, over many miles. Submersibles carried out search and recovery operations but one H-bomb could not be found. The recovery agency

A close-up view of the external instrument package on the bow of the Deepstar 4000. *Technicians check and prepare the craft for its next dive, to explore the ocean floor at 1,219 m (4,000 ft). Among the equipment fit are lights, television cameras, still cameras, sonars and manipulators. (US Navy)*

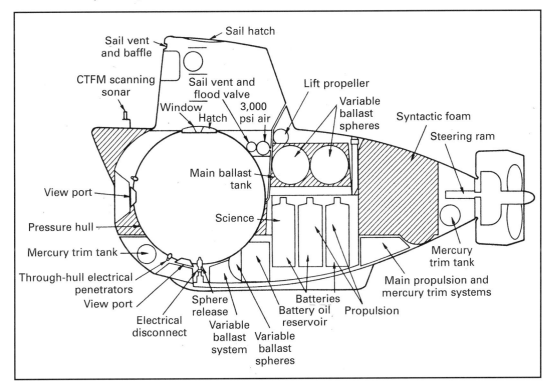

Figure 7: *The* Alvin *submersible, Woods Hole Institution.* (Office of the Oceanographer, US Navy)

sought witnesses and located a Spanish fisherman who had seen an object fall into the sea. The submersibles *Alvin* and *Aluminaut* were sent to the area and carried out a detailed search operation.

They were looking for a cylindrical object 3.6 m (12 ft) x 0.6 m (2 ft) in a water depth of 762 m (2,500 ft), a considerable undertaking in the vast expanse of ocean. *Alvin* completed 34 dives, remaining and operating at depth for 222 hours, with the longest single dive lasting 11 hours. It was on this dive that *Alvin's* team located the bomb, which was resting on the edge of an underwater cliff. While examining the device *Alvin* became entangled in the bomb's parachute, which caused great concern to those in the vehicle and on the surface support vessels. The vehicle was at the end of its normal operational capabilities, its battery power was low and the crew had endured a long dive in difficult circumstances. It was due to a combination of skill and determination on the part of the vehicle's pilot and crew that *Alvin* was eventually freed and a successful recovery of the bomb made.

During a routine dive for a geology study *Alvin* had reached the bottom at 549 m (1,800 ft) when it was attacked by a swordfish weighing some 113.5 kg (250 lb). The fish was so aggressive that its 'sword' penetrated the fibreglass outer shell and wedged the fish on to the submersible. The main hull was comprised of thick steel and the team decided to continue with the dive until a leak detector revealed that there was cause for concern. Then the dive was aborted. Back on board the support vessel, investigations revealed that the attack and the alarm had not been related.

Alvin suffered a worse ordeal when the lifting cables parted while it was being lowered from its support vessel into the water. The pilot was standing on the sail at the time and made good his escape by jumping into the water and swimming clear. Water poured in through the open hatch on to the other two crew members. They were unable to close the hatch because of a control cable passing through it, but they managed to get out before *Alvin* sank to the ocean floor 1,541 m

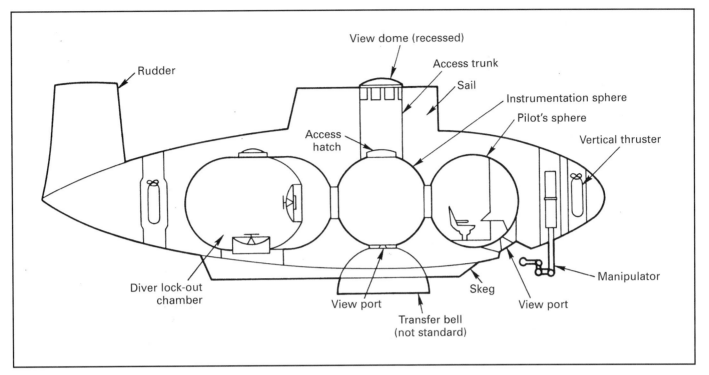

Rudder

View dome (recessed)

Access trunk

Sail

Instrumentation sphere

Pilot's sphere

Vertical thruster

Access hatch

Diver lock-out chamber

View port

Transfer bell (not standard)

Skeg

View port

Manipulator

Figure 8: Deep Quest, *with diver lock-out compartment and transfer system.* (Office of the Oceanographer, US Navy)

(5,052 ft) below. The submersible remained on the ocean floor for almost a year before being salvaged and refurbished prior to becoming operational again.

The research submersible *Deep Quest* was designed to operate at more than 2.4 km (1½ miles) beneath the ocean's surface, on research and design projects both commercial and military. It had a free-flooding outer hull made of welded aluminium alloy which encased the pressure hulls which consisted of two interconnecting steel spheres. An operational depth capability of 2,520 m (8,300 ft) allowed the crew of two plus three observers to undertake a wide and varied range of tasks, including the recovery of seabed samples or the placing of scientific instruments. Two manipulators, each controlled individually, helped with these tasks. A six-barrelled coring device was fitted and could obtain six 1.2 m (4 ft) long core samples at a depth of 2,440 m (8,000 ft). Other specialist equipment in the form of modules was designed and developed for use with the vehicle. The modules included a recovery unit, to allow total saturation lock-out diving, and a replenishment module for resupplying dry underwater habitats.

Deep Quest was also involved in work with prototype systems for the salvage and recovery of objects 1.52 m (5 ft) in diameter and 6.1 m (20 ft) in length from the ocean floor. A device for grabbing objects on the seabed was fitted to the underside of the vessel and controlled from inside the pressure hull. When the object had been grabbed, the submarine could either use its own buoyancy to lift the object, up to a weight of 909 kg (2,000 lb), or the grabbing device could attach a wire to the object, which would allow something weighing up to 86,000 kg (19,000 lb) to be recovered from the seabed at the craft's maximum operating depth.

One innovation on *Deep Quest* was the control system which could be operated either manually or fully automatically. The latter allowed the submarine to follow a pre-determined course which was a valuable asset when undertaking detailed search missions.

The pilot had good forward vision when at the control unit, where he had to be in a prone position. Whilst underwater the crew of *Deep Quest* had full communications with their surface support craft, even when working at maximum operating depth. The vehicle was fitted with two

Right *The Perry Cubmarine was a well-equipped submersible. Its high-powered lights illuminated a wide field of view, and the operators had 360° vision through the all-round view ports. It was fitted with a manipulator which can be seen below the bow of the vehicle. (US Navy)*

Below *A submersible operator looks through the hemisphere port of Deep View from the control position. This was the first submersible to have part of the pressure hull made out of glass. The arm at the bow is able to collect samples. The pods underneath the main submersible contain the batteries which provide the power supply to the vehicle. (US Navy)*

transponders, which allowed the surface vessel to track it while it was submerged.

As we have already seen, the design of submersible vehicles has varied widely over the years, dependent upon their operational requirements. The search for oil and gas in deep water saw the development of more unusual vehicles.

Oceaneering International, a major diving contractor with operations worldwide, developed the concept of a new type of underwater working vehicle, the ARMS. It was built by Perry Oceanographics in the USA and was based upon diving bell principles, being a sealed sphere able to carry a crew of two at atmospheric pressure. It was designated an observation/manipulator bell with three models available dependent upon operational depth requirements. The ARMS which was delivered to Oceaneering was based upon the middle option and had an operating depth capability of 915 m (3,000 ft).

Although the bell was permanently tethered to the surface, it only used its wire cable for lift purposes during launch and recovery operations. In the water, manoeuvring was undertaken using two battery-powered thrusters carried in the

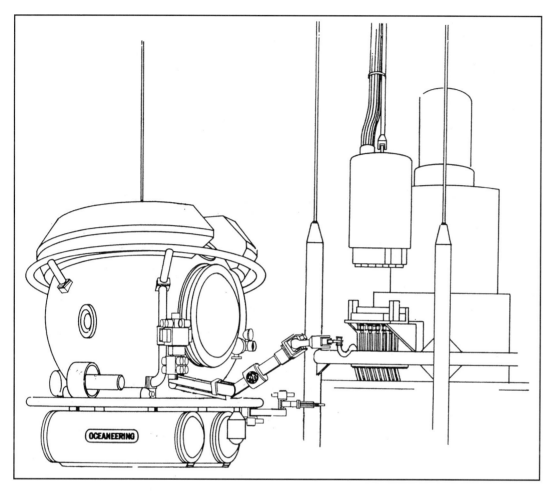

Figure 9: *The Oceaneering ARMS.* (Jane's Ocean Technology)

Far left Oceaneering International's ARMS on board a support vessel. The large domed view port forms a considerable proportion of the front of the bell. The manipulator and underwater television camera are fitted below the port. (Oceaneering)

Left ARMS-IV, belonging to Can-Dive, provides a good view of a thruster and the equipment pods below the bell. (Oceaneering)

equipment pack on the underside of the bell. A unique development in ARMS was the combination of a manipulator and a positioning arm. The function of the arm was to grip an underwater structure or object so that the bell could be held on location. The operators could therefore 'fly' the bell, using the thruster propulsion, to the work location, then select an

attachment point and activate the arms to grip it and 'lock on', thus securing the bell.

The operators were able to observe operations through the single 76 cm (30 in) spherical port and three 15 cm (6 in) view ports, the only restriction on visibility being the clarity of the water. The bell was equipped with television cameras which recorded events on to video tape, a development that was to become a major item of equipment for all future underwater operations. Apart from the observation role, the manipulator provided the bell with the ability to undertake work functions, relying on the skill of the operator.

The manipulator was based upon the human arm principle in that it had a fixed point on the bell from which it was able to pivot. It had a joint which offered limited dexterity and at the end of the arm was the hand, which for most operations consisted of an open and close clamp system, allowing objects to be lifted for placement or recovery. The ingenuity of underwater engineers enabled tools to be designed for specific tasks and fitted as required, and all operations of the manipulator were controlled from inside the bell.

It was apparent to designers and operators that the ARMS concept could be further extended to carry observers and divers to work sites, so the Mobile Diving Unit (MDU) evolved. This system was rated to a depth capability of 305 m (1,000 ft) and was constructed in three parts. There were two bells, one on top of the other. The top bell was the observation bell and was maintained at atmospheric pressure. It had a crew of three who were responsible for the onboard equipment, flying operations and supervising the divers. The lower bell carried two or three divers and could be maintained at atmospheric pressure before being equalized to pressure equal to that of the surrounding water. This would allow the divers to 'lock out' for diving work tasks if they were required. The third part of the system was the life support equipment and propulsion unit.

The observers had a large 75 cm (30 in) panoramic view port which allowed a

Figure 10: *The Perry Mobile Diving Unit (MDU).* (Jane's Ocean Technology)

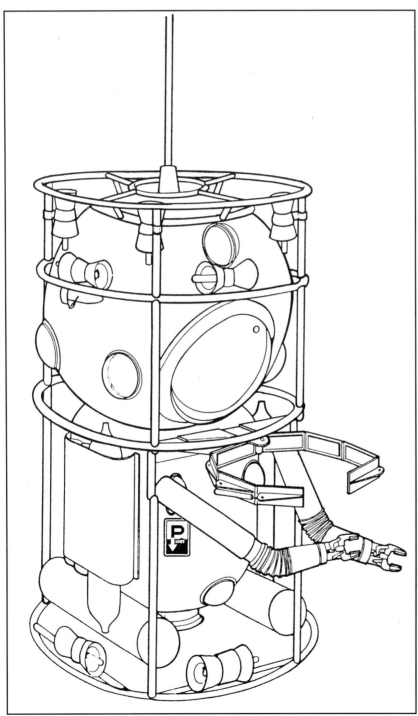

good view of the work site and of the divers when committed to the water. In addition there were a number of 25 cm (10 in) and 15 cm (6 in) view ports which between them offered virtually all-round visibility. Manoeuvring the unit was undertaken from the observation bell using the ten hydraulically powered thrusters. This was an upgrade on the thruster power available to ARMS but it did mean that the main power supply was provided from the surface vessel through an umbilical, leaving the onboard battery power for emergencies.

In operation the MDU was deployed on a main lifting wire. Once at depth the operators could use the thruster propulsion to 'fly' the unit to the desired location. If the unit needed to rest on the seabed it had retractable legs which were extended to keep it clear of the bottom, so allowing the divers easy access to lock out. When working on an underwater structure the MDU could be attached to it using the same system as that fitted to ARMS, and again, it offered a safe, stable diving platform.

The research and development of small submarines has been led for the most part by the needs of the military. The British submarine builder Vickers Shipbuilding designed a small submarine, designated 'Piranha', for covert military operations.

However, it could readily be adapted for commercial or research projects.

The submarine was designed to carry a crew of seven, though in a commercial application it could carry up to ten researchers or a mixture of personnel and scientific equipment. If divers were required they could be 'locked out' to undertake work programmes, but their operations would be restricted as no decompression facilities were available. Due to the overall size of the submarine it would not have been viable to have those facilities fitted. It would have been better to carry remotely operated vehicles (ROVs) which could be controlled from within the submarine and would be able to undertake small research operations away from the parent craft.

The 'Piranha' class submarine was designed with an overall length of 26.6 m (88.66 ft) and an outside diameter pressure hull of 2.75 m (9.16 ft). By necessity, the propulsion machinery system was compact, and because of the restricted space it had to be reliable and efficient, for there was little room to undertake repairs during an operation. A combined motor and generator unit could either be used to drive the propeller when the submarine was submerged, or as a generator, driven by the diesel engine when snorting or surface recharging. The engine contemplated

Below left The Comex MOB 1000 is a mobile observation bell with a depth capability of 1,000 m (3,300 ft). It carries two pilot/observers who remain at atmospheric pressure. At depth the vehicle can manoeuvre within a 500 m (1,650 ft) radius of the mother ship. The pilots control the movement by means of eight propellers. At the work site, the pilots can observe or undertake work functions using the two manipulators. (Alain Tocco, Comex)

Below With limited depth capability and restricted use, the hull inspection platform Dragonfly is lowered into the water. The operator/observer remained at atmospheric pressure and had large view ports for observation. For movement it relied on the support vessel's crane following instructions passed from the operator in the vehicle. (US Navy)

was a unidirectional marine diesel that could be used to drive the propeller or the motor generator, and it was adapted for use with the snort, as is common in large submarines. All mechanical and electrical machinery was supported on flexible rubber mounts to reduce noise, which travels great distances through water and could affect scientific instruments. Submerged power came from the battery, which was sub-divided into two sections of 120 lead acid cells each; these were to be situated below the accommodation spaces forward and aft.

To aid the submarine's operations, a standard sensor fit would include a passive sonar, bow-mounted cylindrical array periscope, radar receiver and noise monitoring sonar. Communications would be provided through transceivers and antennae which allow transmission and reception in the HF and UHF bands.

Fully equipped for an operation, the 'Piranha' would have an overall operating range of some 1,800 nautical miles, at a cruising speed of 7 knots. Submerged and powered by the battery, it had a maximum speed of 9 knots, but this would only be used in an emergency as it would rapidly deplete the power availability. The normal submerged operating speed would be 4 knots, and the power supply would provide a range of 70 nautical miles before recharging was required. In its fully stored and equipped mode, an operational duration of 12 days would be possible.

Further development of this type of submarine could take scientists to research sites where they have previously used habitats. It would eliminate the need for surface diving support vessels and would not be weather-dependent. The submarine could be prepared in the nearest port, enabling the vessel to travel to and from the work site submerged.

Tourism

The deep oceans offer scientists a new world of discovery which unfurls in the laboratory, more often than not under a microscope. There are projects which grip the imagination, such as the exploration of deep ocean wrecks where machines can send us pictures and recover artefacts. Much of the sea's great beauty is found in shallow water, in particular around reefs, and that is now being opened up to those who are unable to scuba dive to visit such sites. Tourist submarines are being established at prime holiday resorts in the more exotic locations, where the underwater world is at its best. Atlantis Submarines of Canada are a world leader in the design, development and building of tourist submarines and provide an insight into the experience that can be gained from these submarines:

From the moment the quiet, electrically-powered submersible glides downward, the magic begins to unfold. Spacious viewing ports allow an intimate look at sights previously seen only on film or considered the domain of the diver. Treasures of the sea are revealed as the adventurers of all ages are guided through this seemingly weightless environment . . . You are riding in the air-conditioned comfort and security of a very real submarine 46 m (150 ft) below the surface. Only the informative and entertaining onboard commentary connects your fantasy with reality. Your experienced pilot and attendant, assisted by the crew in the surface support vessel, take you on a cruise that may take you past towering reefs, wrecks or archaeological remains for an experience you will remember for a lifetime.

Large windows provide excellent viewing for each passenger and the manoeuvrability of the submarine places the passengers within 1.2 to 1.5 m (4–5 ft) of the seabed or reef. For night dives 22 exterior floodlights illuminate the surroundings. Since commencing operations in December 1985, Atlantis submarines have carried more than 2,500,000 passengers on more than 100,000 dives without a single safety-related accident. The Atlantis is a free-swimming, self-propelled submarine capable of operating at a depth of 46 m (150 ft). The vessel is positively buoyant, and is driven down in the water by vertically mounted thrusters. In the event of a power failure, the submarine would automatically rise to the surface.

What is seen from an Atlantis submarine will differ from day to day and in each location, but every tour is pre-planned and is described by the following:

The passengers' experience starts with a short trip by surface boat to the dive site and transfer to the submarine. After all are seated, the hatch is closed. The aircraft-style passenger area is air-conditioned, large enough to stand in, and maintained at normal atmospheric pressure. The 48 passengers sit back to back on moulded seats and face close set, 50.8 cm (20 in) diameter viewing ports, complete with fish identification charts. The pilot is positioned in front of a 127 cm (50 in) acrylic view port. The attendant provides an introduction and demonstration of the safety features of the craft.

The tour starts with a descent to 18 m (60 ft) and moves through coral reefs at the 18–24.3 m (60–80 ft) level, proceeding to deeper areas up to 46 m (150 ft) below the surface. The attendant, experienced in marine biology, provides a running commentary on the fish, corals and underwater vegetation. Brightly coloured fish are abundant and sightings of turtle, barracuda, shark and grouper are possible. Sightings are aided by an underwater feeding pro-gramme, conducted by scuba divers alongside the submarine. As the tour proceeds the submarine works back to shallower depths and after 50 minutes returns to the surface, where the surface boat is waiting to exchange the experienced underwater travellers for a new group ferried from shore.

At the time of writing, Atlantis submarines are operating in the Cayman Islands; Barbados; St Thomas, U.S.V.I.; Kona and Oahu, Hawaii; Guam; Aruba; and the Bahamas.

Bruker, the German submersible builder, has used its extensive know-how to develop the Seamaid tourist submarine, which is basically of the same general configuration as the Atlantis. The Seamaid can carry 50 passengers to a depth of almost 150 m (492 ft), and is fitted with a submersible flange for the transfer rescue of passengers in the event of an accident (see 'Deep ocean rescue' below). Bruker have also included many of the safety features and equipment normally reserved for their deep submergence vehicles and diver 'lock out' submarines, making the 'Seamaid' one of the safest submarines in operation. At the time of writing a

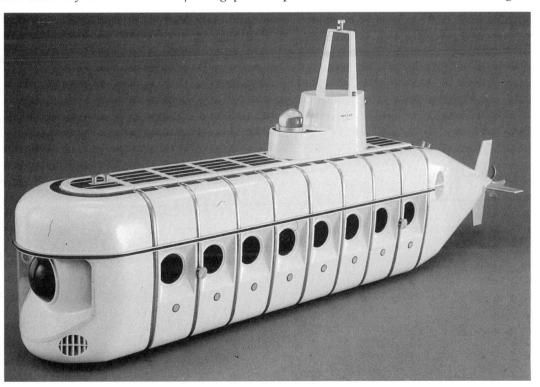

A model of the Bruker 'Seamaid' class tourist submarine, which can carry 50 passengers to a depth of 150 m (492 ft). The passengers are seated two by two in front of large panoramic view ports, which give everyone a good view of the surrounding waters. (Bruker)

Figure 11: *Deep
Submergence Rescue
Vehicles (DSRV) 1 and 2.
(Office of the
Oceanographer, US Navy)*

*A DSRV rescue mission
can be undertaken from
either a surface support
vessel or a submerged
mother submarine. The
system enables crews to
be transferred in the dry
from one vessel to
another. (US Navy)*

'Seamaid' tourist submarine is operating in La Martinique, the French West Indies.

Deep ocean rescue

The one thing that has to be considered above all others when placing people underwater in submersible vehicles is their recovery or rescue in an emergency. It is one thing to work in the controlled environment of a busy oil and gas production industry in the UK North Sea, where resources are available to deal with emergencies. It is however quite a different matter to be operating in remote regions, where help is probably many days away. Rescue capabilities from greater depths will become a major consideration for the future if more manned submersibles become available. This means that submarines both large and small, civilian and military, which can dive deeper and stay submerged longer, carry more people and undertake voyages which can last months, remote from support bases, create untold problems for those who have to go to their aid in the event of an accident.

The US Navy saw the need for deep submergence rescue, by rapid intervention anywhere in the world, for their fleet of military submarines. In order to overcome the problem they developed the Deep Submergence Rescue System which enhanced the technology of small submergence vehicles. Two vehicles evolved – the DSRV One (unofficial name *Mystic*) and the DSRV Two (unofficial name *Avalon*). A total of six DSRVs were planned but funding was only made available for two vehicles. They are normally based in San Diego, USA, where they undertake the DSRV's primary role, that is, to provide world-wide rescue cover for US submarines. As a secondary role they provide world-wide cover for other selected nations' submarines.

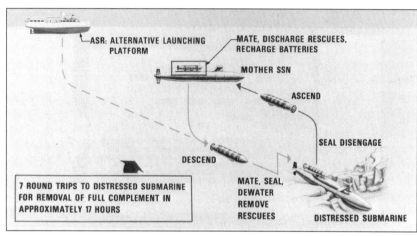

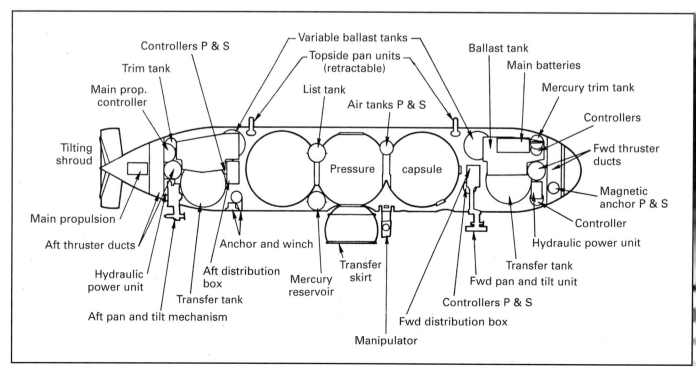

A DSRV has a crew of four, a pilot, a co-pilot and two rescue sphere operators. It can carry up to 24 rescued submariners in a series of shuttle trips, transferring them to a parent submarine whilst remaining submerged or surfacing and transferring them to a surface support vessel. It can continue to operate rescue trips until all of the men in the stricken submarine are rescued.

The outer hull of the DSRV is constructed of fibreglass and surrounds three steel interconnected spheres which form the main pressure capsule. The forward sphere contains the vehicle's control system and is where the pilot and co-pilot are located. One of the other two spheres accommodates the rescued personnel with the third sphere containing the motors, sonars, life support system, batteries and ancillary equipment. The DSRVs can operate at depths of up to 1,525 m (5,000 ft), at a speed of up to 4 knots.

To mobilize a DSRV in an emergency to any part of the world requires it to be fully air portable. For this purpose they each have their own trailer and can be carried in larger transport aircraft such as the C141 or C5. After landing at an airfield close to a suitable sea port the vehicle can then be taken by road to the port where it can be fitted and locked on to a nuclear-powered submarine, or placed on a surface support vessel with the capability to

launch and recover it when at sea. For this purpose the US Navy has two dedicated 'Pigeon' class Submarine Rescue Ships, the USS *Pigeon* and the USS *Ortoland*. Each vessel is able to deploy, recover and service the two DSRVs, but can have the disadvantage of having to undertake a long sea voyage to support a rescue operation. Therefore all US submarines, as well as those of many other nations, are DSRV capable and so a DSRV can be trans-

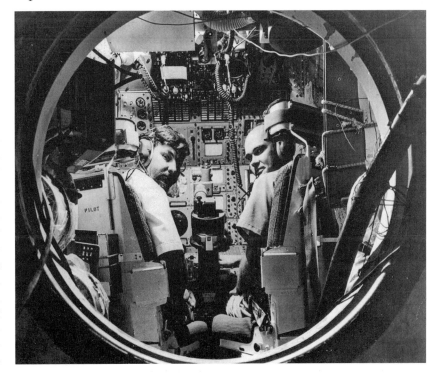

The Sea Cliff *submersible being taken to assist in the search for and recovery of an F14 Tomcat fighter aircraft. The submersible is used primarily for military operations, but it has also undertaken scientific research dives to depths of 1,980 m (6,500 ft). (US Navy)*

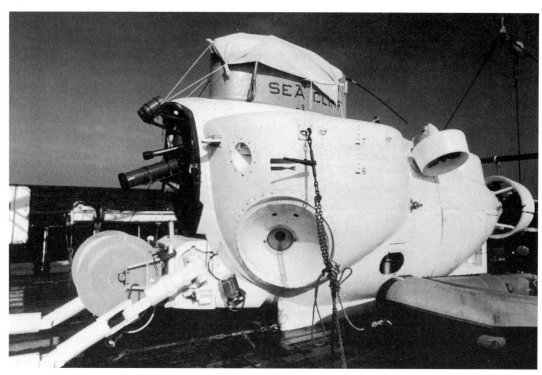

ported by submarine if the surface vessels are unavailable.

The rescue ships are also fitted with deep sea saturation diving systems which will support divers working at depths up to 259 m (850 ft). To ensure that a rapid intervention can be undertaken the US Navy conducts regular exercises around the world, often operating with different navies and their submarines. The decision as to whether a surface rescue ship or a submarine will be used to effect a rescue will depend upon the availability of vessels and submarines, their location and the time required to get to the site of the stricken submarine. Equally important will be the weather conditions in the operational area.

The Royal Navy are included in the US Navy's rescue system but decided that with the time factors involved in mobilizing a DSRV from the USA they would develop their own rescue submarine capability which would operate from a purpose-built seabed operations vessel. Initial trials were carried out in 1975 in the USA with the result that a rapid intervention and rescue capability was found in the form of the Vickers manned submersible *LR5*. After the demise of Vickers' submersible operations, it remained on stand-

by in Aberdeen, Scotland, owned by a commercial company and operated by a civilian crew who were under contract to the British Ministry of Defence. The Royal Navy's Seabed Operations vessel has been removed from service, so there would be a reliance on a number of commercial dynamic positioned diving support vessels that are available and could support manned submersible operations.

The rescue of a submarine's crew is a complicated and risky business and the initiation of a lost submarine emergency will come either from the submarine itself, through a radio transmission, or through its failure to maintain communication at pre-determined times. It could also be reported if a surface vessel was in collision with a submarine. Once an emergency has been declared, the first task is to determine the exact location of the stricken submarine, for time will be a vital factor in the submariners' survival. The various units required to mount a search and rescue operation will be alerted and aircraft dispatched to the area where the vessel is known to be, or to the general area if no definite position is available.

Surface ships will also be directed to the area where they will attempt to locate and communicate with the submarine. They

Far left The extraction of oil and gas from below the North Sea has had to endure some of the worst weather conditions in the world. The base of this type of platform is provided with a series of holes designed to break up the powerful wave force.

Left The worst oilfield disaster ever occurred when the 'Piper Alpha' platform was destroyed. The diving team were working from the lower level and air divers were in the water when the disaster began. With the sea on fire and debris falling all around, the divers were recovered to the surface and the entire diving team made good its escape. This photograph shows the platform in earlier days.

Underwater Exploration

Far left The 'jack-up' drilling rig 'Britannia' is sited alongside a small Conoco platform in the southern North Sea. The two air diving baskets can be seen located between the rig and the platform. This would allow diving to be conducted on either structure in order to provide support and maintenance programmes. It is worth noting that the deck of the rig is some 21 m (70 ft) above the sea. The divers have to be lowered this distance to undertake a dive. (Oceaneering)

Left A closer view of the air diving system on the 'jack-up' drilling rig. The diving baskets have dedicated winches. While one basket is used for the diving operation, the other remains available for emergency purposes. The white container is the dive control, from where the diving supervisor can see the work site. (Oceaneering)

Right *During the
construction of North Sea oil
production platforms, large
accommodation vessels
were moored alongside the
platforms. These provided
stable locations for saturation diving systems. The
system shown here com-
prises two large living
chambers with a smaller
transfer chamber in
between. The diving bell is
locked on top of the transfer
chamber. A dedicated lifting
system is used for the
deployment and recovery of
the bell. Before the bell is
launched it is connected to
the support frame, which
contains an emergency gas
supply and keeps the bell
clear of the seabed, allowing
the divers to leave and enter
the bell. The white box-
shaped container is the dive
control. Situated above the
life support equipment, it
provides a good view of the
dive site.*

Right *This artist's
impression shows an oilfield
with a large production
platform in the background
being supplied with oil
which is recovered from
remote oil wells. The wells
are fitted with a control
system at seabed level which
is protected from possible
damage. Pipelines and
electrical cables link the
wellheads to the platform,
which controls the flow.
Underwater intervention on
modern wellheads is undertaken by ROVs or divers
wearing atmospheric diving
suits.* (Statoil, Norway)

Above left A diver fits a Kirby Morgan Mk 18 helmet with head-mounted television camera. The hot water hose, with water running, hangs clear; it is the last item to be connected. The equipment at the stern of the boat is used to inspect the welds of the platform. The diver's task will be to set it up at the work site. (Oceaneering)

Above A close-up of two divers preparing to dive wearing Kirby Morgan Mk 17 helmets. The helmets are fitted with underwater television cameras and lights. The TV pictures are relayed to the diving supervisor's control console, where he can observe work progress and make a video recording for reporting purposes.

Left A diver wearing a Kirby Morgan band mask undertakes underwater oxy-arc cutting. A mixture of expired breathing gas and expelled oxygen forms bubbles around the work site. In oxy-arc, electrical power is provided to an electrode and oxygen is supplied as a fuel. The combination causes heat sufficient to cut through steel, and is the most common method of cutting used underwater, being efficient and cost-effective. (Rockwater)

Right *The Drager Closed Circuit Breathing System (CCBS) is a compact unit, comprising the helmet and backpack emergency life support unit. The umbilical can be seen at the front of the diver and connects to the diver's system and hot water suit. There is also a hose to carry the expired gas back to the surface. The helmet is connected to the backpack with two hoses which means that if the main gas supply is interrupted, the diver has a minimum of 10 minutes' breathing at 600 m (1,968 ft). Among the many features of the CCBS is gas heating to warm the normally very cold helium gas mix. (Drager)*

Far right *Marine growth adds colour and delicate patterns to offshore structures but it can camouflage damage. To ensure the integrity of a structure, divers undertake regular inspection and repair programmes. (Gordon Clark)*

Right *Wet welding means that the actual weld is undertaken in the water and not in the dry confines of a habitat. The result is that the weld process is cooled rapidly and this leaves it brittle. A wet weld is acceptable for some less critical tasks. When an anode is replaced, for example, it has to have a good physical contact with the structure, and this can be achieved by wet welding. (Gordon Clark)*

Left *This photograph shows clearly where the marine growth on an off-shore structure has been cleaned by an underwater grit-blasting gun. The clean metal allows detailed inspection by divers using specialist equipment.* (Gordon Clark)

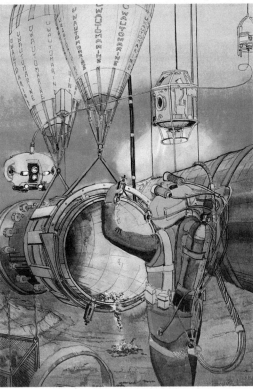

Far left *A diver leaves the diving bell and walks across the seabed to join his colleague, who is guiding a concrete cover into place over a pipeline. Where pipelines cannot be buried, they are at risk from damage by anchors, fishing trawls or dropped objects, so covers are installed which can, if required, be removed at a later date.* (Barry Pearson, Rockwater)

Left *A diver checks a pipe prior to welding. Two lift bags provide support for the pipe to keep it in line and clear of the seabed. The diver was deployed from the diving bell. An ROV keeps the operation under observation.* (Barry Pearson, Rockwater)

Right *A semi-submersible support vessel is positioned above the work site. A diving bell is deployed, allowing two divers to excavate a pipeline. The dredge pump can be seen on the left of the picture. On the right, concrete covers are stored on the seabed ready to be lifted into place over the pipeline when the work is completed.* (Barry Pearson, Rockwater)

Far right *Comex has undertaken research into the use of hydrogen as a breathing mixture for deep diving beyond 250 m (820 ft). Divers undergo a series of practical and speech tests at various depths. Although hydrogen has not yet been adopted for deep diving, it is not ruled out for the future if divers are required to work at depths of up to 1,000 m (3,281 ft).* (Alain Tocco, Comex)

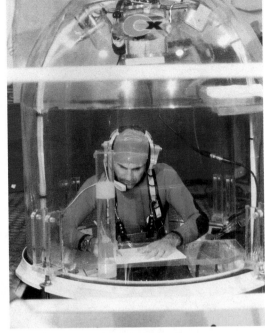

Right *Divers often have to work with rigging equipment that is both heavy and awkward.* (National Hyperbaric Centre)

Right *They are often required to move and set up large, heavy items of equipment, too. Many of the engineering tools they work with have to be used with precision, but this is difficult when working at depth, particularly in murky water.* (Alain Tocco, Comex)

Left *A diver stands inside an experimental chamber where research and experimental work is carried out under pressure on equipment, machines and divers.* (National Hyperbaric Centre)

Left *A diving bell with a side transfer door is prepared for a dive. A large 'A' frame lifts the bell out over the water for launch and recovers it in the same way. A frame on the underside of the bell holds the emergency helium/oxygen gas cylinders and the drop weights.* (Gordon Clark)

Above *The British submersible* LR5 *which is equipped for submarine rescue operations. It is fitted with a range of underwater television cameras and lights. Onboard sonar systems aid underwater search operations. The 'skirt' on the underside is used for mating the submersible to the submarine to allow a dry transfer of personnel.* (Slingsby Engineering)

Above right *An SMD PL2 'Plow' in the launch position at the stern of the support vessel. It is carried there from the deck of the vessel by a large 'A' frame, then lowered to the seabed and towed by the support vessel. The steering feet can be seen at the front end of the plough, close to the vessel. The plough blades are large, and have to cut through various types of seabed to make a trench for the cable, which it then lays and buries.* (SMD)

Right *The 'Eureka' lightweight multi-purpose tracked vehicle, designed and built by SMD, is able to operate in the most harsh sub-sea environments. The vehicle has three trenching tools capable of cable burial in a wide range of soil types from sand through to soft rocks.* (SMD)

Above Comex has been at the forefront of underwater technology ever since its conception in 1961. Engineers at its headquarters in Marseilles, France, have come up with some innovative ideas over the years, like this one, which was a scheme for transporting divers and ROVs to a work site by submarine rather than deploying them from diving support vessels on the surface. Two major advantages would be a reduction in the overall cost of hire, and that a submarine would not be affected by adverse weather. (Alain Tocco, Comex)

Left Moana IV is launched from its support ship. Comex designed and built the submersibles Neree in 1971, the Globule, the Marco and three Moanas in 1974. (Alain Tocco, Comex)

Right *A UFO 350C ROV is deployed into the water. The vehicle is housed in a garage with the remote tether held in a spooling device on the top of the garage. All functions of the ROV and the tether are controlled by the pilot. (Rockwater)*

Far right *A Drager test chamber, showing its ability to open up to its full diameter to allow equipment, including submersibles, access for pressure testing. This type of chamber is a major capital investment for research and tests both depth and altitude pressures. (Drager)*

Right *One of the greatest advantages of the Drager Newt Suit is that its flexible joints allow the operator 75 per cent of a diver's dexterity. This makes it a viable alternative to a large, expensive saturation diving complex, particularly in deep water. The operator has good vision, which could give it the edge over an ROV. The life support system is located in the black box on the back of the suit. (Drager)*

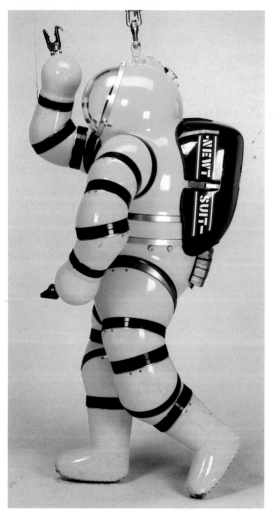

Left *Hull Maintenance Technician 2nd Class/Diver Jacquelyn Himschoot with a sea-lion at the US Navy's Dolphin and Sea-Lion Training Unit. A relationship of trust must be established between human and animal for there to be an effective team.* (US Navy)

Far left *A member of the US Navy Explosive Ordnance Disposal Unit Four trains a dolphin to lead itself into a special boat so that it can be transported to and from work sites. Dolphins are trained to search for and recover objects from the seabed.* (US Navy)

Left *Play time for a dolphin and his trainer, both of whom are with the US Navy's Dolphin and Sea-Lion Training Unit.* (US Navy)

Right *Putting the training undertaken in the pen into practice requires the sea-lion to go out to sea, search for an object and connect a lifting line to it. The training works and a most effective underwater search and recovery system is established.* (US Navy)

Right *The Tektite habitat being prepared to be lowered to the seabed, where teams were to spend periods of up to 60 days in saturation. They lived in the habitat, using diving equipment when they needed to leave it in order to carry out a range of scientific projects.* (US Navy)

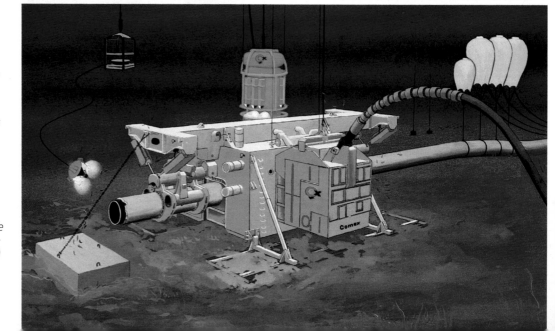

Right *An artist's impression of an underwater welding habitat. The pipeline passes through the habitat, held clear of the seabed. The diving bell remains alongside, being the welder divers' means of transport. Welding creates fumes which have to be extracted, and the correct gas mixture for the depth being worked has to be maintained. The large umbilical carries the hoses and power cables for the life support and welding equipment.* (Alain Tocco, Comex)

Far left *The hyperbaric habitat, showing the pipeline held and sealed in position. Once the habitat is secure the water inside is replaced with gas to create a dry atmosphere. The welder divers gain access by entering through the bottom of the habitat, having been transported to the seabed by a diving bell. The pipeline can then be welded to the highest standards in the same way as it would be on the surface.* (Barry Pearson, Rockwater)

Left *The scene inside a hyperbaric habitat once the water has been removed and replaced by gas. The ends of the pipe have been aligned and clamps fitted, ready for the weld to be made.* (Rockwater)

Left *The Towed Ocean Bottom Instrument (TOBI) is secured to the aft deck of a support vessel. The unit is a deep-towed, flexible instrument platform with excellent stability. It can operate down to a depth of 6,000 m (19,686 ft) and is capable of resolving side-scan targets only 2 m (6.5 ft) across. TOBI's advanced systems have revolutionized the way geologists and geophysicists visualize the seabed and its processes.* (Institute of Oceanographic Sciences, Deacon Laboratory)

Right *The Deep Ocean Long Path Hydrographic Instrument (DOLPHIN), represented here by a small yellow shape on the right of the picture, completes deep water sections across ocean basins, providing complementary information to satellite observations of the surface and to other instruments which monitor the mixed layer of the upper ocean and coastal seas. DOLPHIN can carry out profiles of the ocean from the surface to the seabed, surfacing every 30 km (18.6 miles) to fix its position by the Global Positioning Satellite system, and to relay data to shore stations.* (Institute of Oceanographic Sciences, Deacon Laboratory)

Right *An artist's impression of the Van Oord ACZ flexible fallpipe vessel* Trollness. *The picture shows the vessel on the surface with the flexible pipe extending to the seabed. The specially designed ROV can be seen at the bottom end and is able to direct the flow of rock dumping. In this project, rock is being spread over the seabed to provide a stable base on which a pipeline can be laid.* (Van Oord ACZ)

Left *Man's exploration of outer space and inner space has pursued technological challenges to the very limits. Much of the experience and know-how gained has been used by both those who have launched into the sky and those for whom the oceans hold the ultimate challenge. This dramatic picture brings together the combined efforts of both, but focuses on sub-sea technology in the Shell/Esso Cormorant field in the North Sea. (Shell UK Exploration and Production)*

Left *Biologist Gerard Wellington prepares to dive using a bubble helmet. When underwater he was linked via satellite direct to youngsters who were participating in a Woods Hole Jason Foundation project. (US Navy)*

Right *Dr Robert Ballard of Woods Hole was able to explore the inside of the Titanic using the Jason Junior remote operated vehicle.* (Woods Hole Oceanographic Institute)

Right *The deep submersible vehicle Alvin, fitted with the Jason Junior remote operated vehicle was used by Dr Ballard to explore inside the Titanic.* (Woods Hole Oceanographic Institute)

Right *This exploration of the Titanic was recorded with dramatic pictures.* (Woods Hole Oceanographic Institute)

A port bow view of the nuclear-powered research submersible NR1. It carried a crew of seven and a full range of navigation equipment, television cameras and scientific instruments, and it had an operating ability of 30 days, although with limited facilities. The submersible was fitted with wheels to enable it to crawl on the seabed. Many of its research programmes and operations were secret. (US Navy)

would also be available to rescue the submarine's crew if they decided to abandon the submarine in a 'through water' free ascent escape. The submarine crew will be active and deploy emergency buoys and smoke flares to provide the searchers with a position reference of their location. Maritime patrol search aircraft are able to drop sonar buoys normally used for anti-submarine operations that are capable of locating submerged submarines.

Once the stricken submarine is located the first task is to determine its depth, status of damage and position, information vital for the rescuers so that they can plan the rescue operation and know what to expect. They need to determine the heel angle of the submarine (if the submarine is lying on its side it is impossible to connect the rescue submersible to it), and whether the escape hatches are damaged and/or are still usable. This survey work can be undertaken by divers if the submarine is in a water depth where divers are able to reach and if suitable diving equipment is available. Alternatively, remote operated vehicles can be deployed to relay pictures to the surface.

The divers or ROV will place transponder beacons on the submarine which send signals to the rescue submersible's sonar system. This means that the rescue submersible can locate the submarine and the escape hatches without the need for a search operation. An attempt to communicate with the crew will also be made in order to determine their well-being, the status of their life support system and how many people are to be rescued.

In the worst case the crew may have to abandon the submarine while it lies on the seabed. If the water is too deep to allow a 'free ascent' then they must await a transfer rescue. If conditions dictate that they have to abandon the submarine then a vast expanse of unyielding ocean awaits them and there may be little chance of survival, especially for injured personnel. A 'free ascent' will therefore only be contemplated if it becomes a life or death situation and transfer is not possible.

The rescuers have to consider the number of persons to be transferred and how many can be carried on each transfer dive. They have to decide what life support and first aid equipment needs to be carried to the submarine before the rescue can begin. The rescue submersible will carry additional ballast, which will be equivalent to the weight of the crew to be transferred. This is so that the operations weight of the craft does not alter to the extent that it becomes too heavy or too light.

Once the crew has completed the checks, the rescue submersible will be launched and descend to the stricken submarine. The pilot will be guided to the escape hatch by the transponders, where he will move the craft on to the submarine's casing, aligning it with the escape hatch. To mate the two hatches, the pilot uses underwater video cameras installed underneath the submersible and inside the skirt. Apart from aiding the pilot, this also means that the rescue can be recorded on video tape for future evaluation. Once the submersible is in position the pilot will thrust the vehicle down so that the two sealing faces mate, and drain the water inside the skirt into the submarine's bilges by operating a suction pump. As the pressure reduces, the two joining faces are pulled together to form a seal.

When the pressure has equalized, the hatches of the stricken submarine and the rescue submersible can be opened. The life support and medical equipment are the first items to be transferred. When the first group have moved into the rescue craft all hatches are closed and sealed and the skirt is then flooded to equalize with the surrounding water pressure. The ballast weights can be released which will then free the rescue vehicle and allow it to ascend to the surface and be recovered by the surface support vessel. Once on board the rescued personnel disembark, leaving the rescue craft's crew and support team to prepare for the next dive. These dive sequences continue until all of the stricken submarine's crew are rescued.

As described earlier, the DSRV is designed to be carried 'piggy back' on another submarine, which means that it is not dependent upon surface support vessels or, more importantly, the weather. The rescue operation and procedures are the same for either DSRV to submarine or DSRV to surface vessel.

Chapter 8

Manned Submarines

THE NEED TO deploy divers deeper underwater, beyond the limits of air diving, required the use of saturation diving systems, with bells to transport the divers to and from the seabed. Dynamic positioned vessels (see Chapter 15) were in their infancy and were not generally accepted as far as the offshore oil and gas industry was concerned. This meant that the range of vessels available to divers was very limited. Semi-submersible accommodation rigs provided stable platforms for systems, and while they were moored alongside platforms which were under construction, divers could be deployed. That had its own set of problems because the vessel remained in one place and so restricted the area that divers could reach.

There was a need to inspect and repair existing structures where the costs of such a large support facility were prohibitive. One option adopted was to engage large supply vessels and modify them with additional accommodation and 'add-on' saturation dive systems. To remain in position these vessels were required to lay a four-point anchor mooring, which meant that four anchors were laid at four opposing points of the vessel in order to obtain an even pull. In this manner the vessel could be held on location. Other vessels lay two bow anchors and placed the stern on to the structure, securing the vessel to the platform with mooring ropes. This system was suitable for air diving operations but not for saturation diving because the ves-

Figure 12: *Sous-Marin D'Intervention Submarine.* (Jane's Ocean Technology)

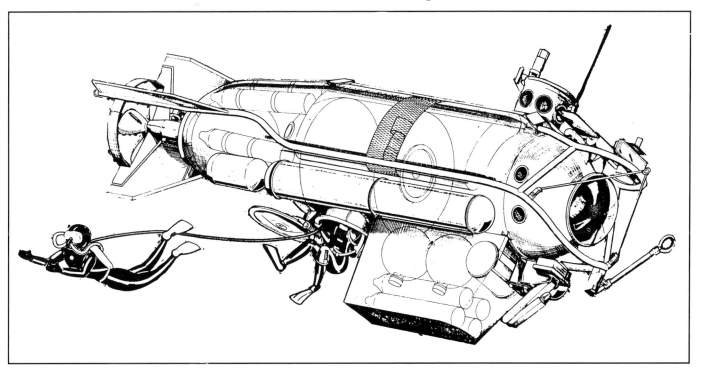

sels were too heavy. The anchoring and mooring systems were effective, but time-consuming and very weather-dependent.

In a bid to overcome these problems the industry introduced small submarines from which divers, in saturation, could be taken to the work site and could 'lock out' in order to undertake the underwater work projects. Submarine support vessels were required and that meant rapid conversions. Some were converted from large supply boats, but the best were former freezer trawlers. Their original design and size meant that they could easily be converted to take the additional accommodation and had adequate space in which to install saturation chambers and the control and support equipment. The stern area also provided space for a hangar where the submarines could be stored and maintenance carried out in dry conditions. Equally important was the fact that they had been designed to operate in extreme weather conditions and so had excellent sea-keeping capabilities.

Most of the diver 'lock-out' submarines carried a crew of two, who occupied the forward sphere and were maintained at atmospheric pressure. One of these was the pilot, who was in overall command of the vehicle. He sat at the control console at the bow, where the large acrylic spherical port provided good forward vision. With him was the diving supervisor, who controlled the diving operation. From his position he could also look out of the port and watch the divers at work. He could liaise freely with the pilot (a very useful thing when the latter's actions could affect the well-being of the divers) and communicate with the divers both when they were in the submarine and in the water. The divers' pressure chamber was independent of the forward sphere apart from the communication system, and was held at a pressure equal to the outside water pressure. Two divers were carried, allowing one man to 'lock out' and go to work while the other remained in the submarine to tend the diver's umbilical and be available to go to his aid in an emergency.

During the late '60s and early '70s a number of companies established themselves in the manned diver lock-out sub-

The submarine 'Ben Franklin' was designed by Dr Jacques Piccard in 1968. It could operate to a depth of 606 m (2,000 ft) with a crew of six. Three of the crew carried out the operational functions, leaving the remaining three to observe and record the experiments. One of the major experiments undertaken involved monitoring the Gulf Stream drift. (US Navy)

marine market. It was 1969 when Vickers Oceanics began their first operations in the North Sea, and by 1978 they had created a fleet of nine submersibles and five support vessels. The Vickers submersibles included three 'Pisces' class, designated *II*, *III* and *VIII*, and four 'PC15' class, designated *LR1*, *LR2*, *LR3* and *LR5*. The 'Pisces' submarines had a crew of two and could operate to depths of 730 to 1,000 m (2,400-3,280 ft), but they were only used for manned observation and manipulator operations, and did not have diver 'lock-out' facilities. Because they carried man underwater they were bound to attract public interest if there was an accident, and it so happened that the only submarine to require rescue from the seabed did not carry divers. There were near misses, but the following incident highlights the risks and support involved.

It was not by choice that Vickers Oceanics made the headlines when disaster struck, sending one of their submersibles to the seabed, and a major rescue operation began. The incident began on Wednesday 29 August 1973,

when the deep submersible vehicle (DSV) *Pisces III* sustained flooding of the after machinery compartment and sank to the seabed in 419 m (1,375 ft) of water some 100 miles southwest of Ireland. Trapped inside the main sphere of the vehicle were pilots Roger Mallison and Roger Chapman, who were both well and had about 72 hours of life support available.

Pisces III was under charter, performing tasks associated with the laying of a telephone cable from Ireland to Nova Scotia in Canada. Initial notification of the accident was received at the Naval Ocean Systems Center (NOSC), San Diego, on the Wednesday, with a request for information on the status of the *CURV III* remote operated vehicle. Vickers had appealed to the US Navy for backup assistance to their primary plan to raise the distressed submersible with the aid of her sister vehicles, *Pisces II* and *V*, which were being airlifted to the scene of the accident.

CURV III was the third in a series of unmanned remotely controlled vehicles developed by NOSC primarily for use in the recovery of test ordnance. However,

The manned submersible LR1 was fitted with a 'skirt' to enable it to connect to a large submarine's hatch and transfer its crew at atmospheric pressure. This class of submersible was employed for diver lock-out operations, with a crew of three operators and two divers. For observation tasks it had a depth capability of 366 m (1,200 ft), but for diver lock-out operations it was restricted to the divers' operating depth of about 122 m (400 ft). (Royal Navy)

like her predecessor *CURV I*, which had played a major role in the recovery of the hydrogen bomb off Palomares, Spain, in 1966, *CURV III* had been developed to respond to emergency situations. The vehicle and its associated equipment was transferred from its primary support ship to the dock at the Naval Air Station, North Island (San Diego), where all components were placed on pallets in preparation for aircraft loading by 14:30 hrs Wednesday. Two US Air Force C-141 Starlifter aircraft transported the vehicle, its support equipment, and crew direct from North Island to Cork, Ireland, arriving at 19:30 hrs on Thursday 30 August. At Cork, the equipment was unloaded from the aircraft, transferred to a barge at the dock, and taken to the Canadian cable-laying ship *John Cabot*, which was lying about 16 km (10 miles) down the river since low tide prevented her approaching the dock. By Friday, all of the *CURV* equipment and crew were embarked, allowing the *John Cabot* to proceed to the accident site, arriving late on the Friday.

A recovery attachment device manufactured by Vickers consisting of a large toggle bolt was provided to the US Navy crew for use on the *CURV*. Since the after hatch of *Pisces III* was open, the easiest place to make an attachment for lifting the submersible was through this hatch. Most of the submersible was covered by a fibreglass fairing, which could not sustain the loads needed for lifting. Since the vehicle had sunk when the after machinery compartment flooded, it was sitting tail down with the hatch opening in a perpendicular plane. A 203 mm (8 in) circumference double-braided nylon line was attached to the toggle bolt, then taped (with low-strength masking tape) to the *CURV* frame, and taped at intervals all along the tether cable.

On the Saturday morning (1 September) a Vickers representative requested that the *CURV* be sent to *Pisces III* to attempt to attach the heavy lift line. Shortly after, *CURV* was deployed over the side and ready to dive. Arriving on the bottom at a depth of 457 m (1,500 ft), the vehicle commenced a 360° sonar scan until a

large sonar target was detected. The sonar target was closed, and through the onboard television cameras was identified as *Pisces III*. Using the manipulators, the toggle bolt was placed in position and secured by observing it via the television cameras.

A strain was put on the lift line by the *John Cabot*, causing the tool holder to be ejected from the *CURV* manipulator and the masking tape ties to break as the lift cable separated from the *CURV* tether. The lift of *Pisces III* had begun. The submersible was raised to the surface where an additional line was attached by swimmers so that it could be held horizontally to allow the crew to get out.

Once the craft was secure the men climbed out and were transferred, in good condition, via rubber boat to the *Vickers Voyager*. Although 70 hours had passed since the start of the initial dive and the life support system was designed for 72 hours' duration, it was estimated that the two men could have safely remained within the submersible for an additional 12-15 hours. Both men in *Pisces III* were experienced and they had exercised considerable restraint during their wait for rescue by relaxing, sleeping, and taking other measures to reduce their metabolic rate, thereby conserving the oxygen supply and the carbon dioxide absorbent.

The water was pumped out of the after machinery compartment, and *Pisces III* was then returned to the *Vickers Voyager*, thus completing not only the rescue of the two pilots but also the salvage of the submersible. The *John Cabot* returned to Cork where the *CURV* system was offloaded, transferred to the airfield and the two C-141 aircraft, and returned to the NOSC San Diego home base.

The Perry PC diver 'lock-out' class submersibles operated by Vickers Oceanics were designed in the USA. In this design the main sections are of modular construction, with the pressure chambers bolted together and then encased in a streamlined fairing. The modules provide the three main components of a control chamber, a divers' compression chamber and a propulsion module. The fact that they are interchangeable means that if one

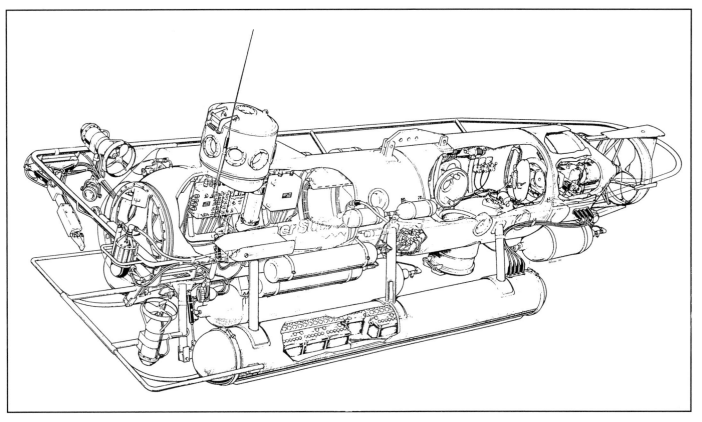

Figure 13: *Perry PC diver lock-out submarine.* (Jane's Ocean Technology)

section needs upgrading it can easily be replaced.

The design of the vehicle includes two battery pods that extend the length of the craft and provide natural skids when sitting on the seabed or the deck of the support vessel. The pilot sits behind a 50.8 mm (2 in) thick hemispherical dome 1.07 m (3 ft 6 in) in diameter. The batteries are fitted on removable trays which can be drawn out and replaced in about two hours. These submersibles can operate in depths of 366 m (1,200 ft) to 457 m (1,500 ft).

The Vickers *LR4* was a glass-reinforced plastic, pressure-hulled submersible with a dive depth of 457 m (1,500 ft), and whilst it was able to operate with diver lock-out, it could also be fitted with a skirt on the bottom hatch. This would allow the small submarine to lock on to a large submarine to allow crew transfer in a rescue operation.

The P & O Sub Sea Submersible Company operated the 'Mermaid III' and 'IV' class of submersibles which were designed and built by the German company Bruker Meerestechnik GmbH. The body of the submarine was cylindrical and contained a pilot and supervisor's compartment. The top of this section included a conning tower which enabled the pilot to see when the submarine was on the surface. The divers had their own separate pressure compartment which had a hatch on the bottom to allow them access to the water. The batteries were stored in two cylindrical pods running the length of the submarine and contained lead acid batteries which provided the power for the main electric motor, the hydraulic pump, the heater, a DC converter and a number of searchlights. Propulsion came from a main thruster at the stern which also aided steering, and two horizontal thrusters were installed in the fairing at the stern and another in the conning tower. Two vertical thrusters provided the up and down movement and were placed at the centre of gravity on either side of the craft.

The entire system was controlled by the pilot using a single console with hand controls. Speed was maintained by way of remote controlled flow valves, and an emergency system would surface the craft

Above *Once the submarine is lowered into the water, a diver is put on board to detach the lifting cable. When it is released the diver joins the inflatable boat, allowing the submarine to submerge. (Frank Murray)*

Above right *A Brucker diver lock-out submarine lifted clear of the support ship's deck. The specially developed 'A' frame and handling system moves it clear of the stern for launch into the sea. (Frank Murray)*

automatically if the pilot was incapacitated or if the craft reached a critical depth. Eight high-pressure storage cylinders laid out in two banks provided the air and oxygen necessary to maintain the internal atmosphere for a crew of four for 160 man hours. Two carbon dioxide scrubbers cleaned the atmosphere and aided circulation. For emergency purposes the pilot, supervisor and divers (the latter if not at depth breathing mixed gas) were provided with a nose and mouth breathing system linked into a compressed gas breathing system. Ten cylinders provided the divers' breathing gas, the flow of which was controlled by the supervisor, who directed it to the divers through their umbilicals.

The pilot sat behind a hemispherical dome port, which enabled him to see where he was going, observe the work site and operate the manipulator. It is interesting to note that the heavy manipulator could be jettisoned in an emergency, and if the craft were damaged, hard ballast could be dropped and the ballast tanks blown, which would allow the vessel to rise to the surface even if one of the battery pods flooded. The ballast tanks were designed to provide good stability and freeboard (the amount of the vessel out of the water) which would allow the sub to be towed if bad weather ruled out recovery to the mother ship.

The other principal company operating diver lock-out subs was Intersub. They operated a number of offshore supply vessels converted to carry and operate submarines and were designated *Intersub One, Two* and *Five*, while *Intersub Three* and *Four* were converted from former freezer stern trawlers. All vessels were equipped with a saturation diving complex rated to 350 m (1,000 ft).

The launching and recovery of all submersibles follows similar procedures and is very dependent upon the weather conditions. The craft is mounted on a trolley and moved out on rails to the stern where the main lift wire, which passes through the 'A' frame, is connected to the submarine. Once latched on, the vessel is lifted clear of the deck. Hydraulic rams then push the 'A' frame out over the stern, allowing the submarine to be lowered into the sea. A diver dressed in a diving suit but without underwater breathing equipment is taken to the craft by inflatable boat. Once on board he unhooks the lift wire, allowing the submarine to move away from the parent vessel. The diver is then collected, and the submarine heads towards the structure and submerges.

Once under the water the pilot of the submarine checks the through-water communications with the parent vessel's control room. While the divers are at work the parent vessel steams well clear of the structure and only when the work is completed and the submarine surfaces does it return for the pick-up.

On the surface the submarine needs to be stable, for it is relatively small, and it has a critical recovery operation to undertake. The parent vessel will line itself up to make a run past the submarine at a speed of about 1 1/2 knots. An inflatable with a crew of three is launched from the ship, and they take the tow rope out to the submarine and attach it to the budge bar on the bow. The mother ship continues on course, and the slack in the tow line is taken up to the point where the submarine is actually being towed. The diver can either rejoin the inflatable or ride the submarine in.

As the submarine moves in behind the mother ship, it is winched in. In marginal weather, this can be rather a rough ride for those inside, and whilst the temptation to open the conning tower hatch is probably very great, it has been the cause of submersibles coming to grief in the past when a large wave has swamped the ves-sel. As the submarine moves closer to the stern of the mother ship, the 'A' frame, already lowered to the recovery position, awaits the connection of the lifting wire. With the submarine latched in place the powerful hydraulics lift it on board to place it securely on the trolley. It is then rolled along the rails to the mating flange of the saturation transfer chamber. This is at deck level and a flexible extension is actually raised up to make the connection between the submarine and the saturation complex. Once the pressure is equalized, the divers inside the submarine are able to transfer to the chambers below.

On deck there is plenty of activity as the submersible has to be prepared for the next dive, and that means that the batteries have to be replaced. The batteries are located inside pressure-sealed tubes or pods with an opening hatch at either one end or both ends. When these are opened the batteries, which are on trays, are pulled out and placed on charge for future use. Charged batteries replace them and are connected up and sealed in the tubes or pods, providing a full power supply for the next dive. Equipment function tests are carried out to ensure that everything works, for it is an expensive and time-consuming business to launch a submarine and then find that you have problems.

The pilot is responsible for the submersible and ensures that the function tests are carried out. Those functions will include the main motor, thruster propulsion units and the ballast pumps. Other equipment such as the manipulators, TV cameras and lights are also checked. The diving supervisor will carry out function tests with the pressurized diver compartment, to ensure that there is sufficient breathing gas and that it is of the correct mixture. The divers' hot water heater must work and is therefore checked.

Communications are vital, and that means both ways between the supervisor and the diver in the water as well as the diver in the submersible. During the dive the diver may find something that requires the representative of the company which owns the structure to make a decision and so communications between the sub-

The Inner Space Porpoise 1000 twin-hose rebreather backpack assembled ready for use. Divers needed a closed-circuit system to provide their breathing gas because submersibles were unable to carry sufficient gas for open circuit. (Frank Murray)

transfer up into the pressurized dives compartment. The submarine's internal door is closed, as is the systems entrance lock door, and the pressure in the trunking is reduced until it is at atmospheric pressure and can be disconnected from the submersible. The launching process is then carried out again to begin the next diving operation.

A diver working at depth can consume a considerable quantity of gas, which can cause problems if that gas has to be carried on board the submarine. Intersub provided the answer by using the Porpoise 1000 twin-hose heliox closed-circuit breathing system. This was comprised of two flasks of gas, one oxygen, the other helium, and a container for the carbon dioxide absorbent for the removal of carbon dioxide, all encased in a pack on the diver's back. The correct mixture of helium and oxygen was sent to the diver automatically. Exhaled breath returned down a separate hose to the carbon dioxide absorbent for cleansing. Because some oxygen would have entered the diver's bloodstream, the return gas percentages would not be correct, which meant that apart from the impurities being removed from the gas, the oxygen content had to be made up. On the other hand, if the mixture became oxygen-rich, helium could be added to dilute it.

Because the system was self-contained, the diver needed to know at any given time what the status of his gas mixture was. To do this his helmet was fitted with a specially designed monitor or gauge, sited on the outside of the helmet at the top of the face plate. Unlike the normal gauge, it had three main points: H = high, N = normal and L = low, and an indicator which moved between them depending upon the content of the gas mixture. It was an LED system which could easily be seen by the diver in daytime or nighttime conditions simply by raising his eyes to look at the top of the face plate. Using the Porpoise system enabled the diver to remain at work for the duration of the dive without drawing any gas from the limited storage carried on the submarine. (The diver did have an umbilical and included in it was a breathing gas hose

mersible and the surface support vessel are also essential.

The divers who are to make the dive will pass through from the saturation complex to the pressure chamber in the submarine. This will allow them to undertake internal checks of the diving compartment and the equipment, to ensure that everything is in good working order, for it is not just lost dive time that could affect them – their lives depend on the equipment.

Once the submersible is deemed ready to dive and the diving supervisor, pilot and divers have been briefed, the divers

Aquadyne helmets were modified to work with the Porpoise 1000 rebreather. A display bar located at the top of the face plate provided three O_2 sensors that enabled the diver to monitor his own breathing supply mixture while locked out of the submersible. (Frank Murray)

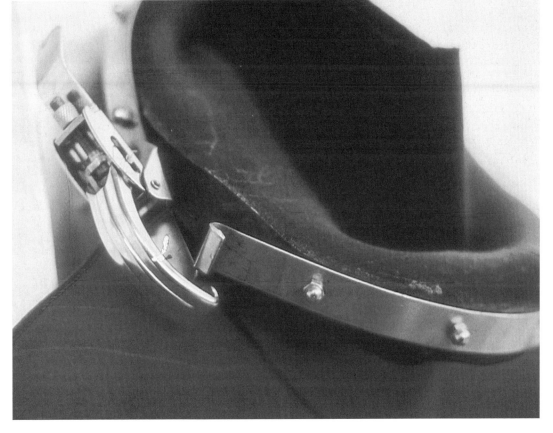

The Aquadyne helmet requires a seal at the neck and in this case the clamp is part of the diver's suit. This means that the diver enters the suit and pushes his head up through the seal. The helmet is then connected to the seal and clamped closed. (Frank Murray)

Right The open container of the Porpoise 1000 rebreather system. The container would be filled with a carbon dioxide (CO_2) absorbent which would clean the expired breath. (Frank Murray)

Far right Once the container is filled with absorbent the holding lid is fitted and only requires the sealing lid to be clamped in place. (Frank Murray)

which was for emergency purposes only. If the system failed, sufficient gas would be available for the diver to return to the submarine safely.)

Another vital item of diver's equipment which required development was the system used to provide warmth for the diver while in the water. The conventional method was, and still is, to heat water on the surface support vessel and pump it down the umbilical to the diver. The diver wears a hot water suit which allows heated water to circulate around his body and then discharge itself into the surrounding water. This system requires a hot water machine which is able to heat considerable quantities of water quickly. Again, the submarine was not capable of producing hot water in this manner and so, using available technology, a closed-circuit hot water system was designed and developed.

The end product was a system where hot water could be produced, circulated around the diver, and then recovered to be reheated and returned to the diver. Producing hot water could not be done using an electric immersion tank-type system as the submarine could not carry

enough battery power to produce sufficient electricity for such an undertaking. The problem was solved by using chemicals which reacted with water to generate heat. This created a supply of hot water which could be pumped from the submarine to the diver and back. However, the water could not be dumped, so a specially designed undersuit was produced. It fitted the whole body and had a web of tubes incorporated into it, with additional tubes in sensitive body areas. The tube system had an inlet valve to allow the hot water to flow in and circulate through the tubes to an outlet valve. From the outlet valve the water returned to the submarine to be reheated before being pumped back to the diver.

Both the gas monitoring system and the heated suit were unique to submarine operations, and they worked. Frank Murray, a diver who used both types of equipment from 'lock-out' submarines, states that they worked efficiently all the time and cannot recall there ever being a problem with either of them.

While small submarines are a successful method of transportation for either observation or diver deployment, a major fail-

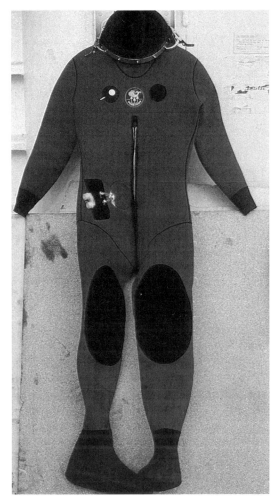

ing has always been the amount of energy source they can carry. Large submarines are equipped with nuclear propulsion, but the small vessels have to rely upon batteries. This has meant that an operation was dependent upon the storage capacity which could be carried and the kilowatt hours available. For extended operations where a surface support vessel was not required, the submarine needed to be self-sufficient and capable of extended voyages. This required an energy source other than batteries alone. In his book *Un Conquérant Sous La Mer*, on the history of Comex, Alain Dunoyer de Segonzac described the company's approach to an innovative submarine engine design. Commander Cousteau designed and began the construction of a mobile undersea habitat which evolved into the submersible *Argyronete*. Due to lack of funds the project remained uncompleted and in storage until Comex took it over. The

development was renamed *Saga 1* and included the latest technical submarine developments.

Comex had undertaken a number of contracts with Swedish companies, including Kockums, who were working on the development of a new engine, called the Stirling. An engine requires oxygen to allow it to operate and an exhaust system to dispose of waste gas, therefore it is not possible to use an internal combustion engine in a submerged submarine. The Stirling engine was developed to overcome these problems and provide an engine that could be used within the confines of a submerged submarine and conserve battery power for emergencies. While Comex had taken the *Saga* project to a successful conclusion with the aid of a number of companies, finance was yet again to become a hurdle which could not be resolved and *Saga* never become operational.

It is evident that air-independent energy sources have become an alternative to battery-powered systems and Bruker Meerestechnik GmbH, already playing a leading role in the field of development and construction of underwater vehicles and special diving systems, therefore did not hesitate to meet the technical challenge when MAN Technologie GmbH suggested co-operation in this field.

Based on the proven Bruker *Seahorse II* submersible, of which two units had

Left A 'uni' diving suit made of a thick neoprene material modified to include a closed-circuit hot water system. (Frank Murray)

Commander Cousteau designed and began the construction of a mobile undersea habitat, the submersible Argyronete. Due to lack of funds, the project remained uncompleted. The hull had been stored and was in perfect condition when Comex took over the project. (Alain Tocco, Comex)

The Argyronete *project was eventually completed by Comex using the latest submarine technology and commissioned as Saga I. Due to high capital costs the vessel never became operational.* (Alain Tocco, Comex)

already been built, an autonomous submarine was built for the purpose of research and involved the concept of an argon closed-cycle diesel engine (CCD) that would allow the engine to be used in a submarine while it was submerged. The vehicle was launched in June 1989 after several years of development, construction and assembly. Besides its role as a platform to test the CCD plant, the submarine was also suited for long-range underwater inspections, and as a vehicle for scientific, locating and navigational instrumentation to be tested.

Perry Offshore Inc. is a US company which has extensive experience in the research and development of subsea vehicles, both military and commercial. They developed the 'PC' class of diver 'lock-out' submarine, which was operationally successful in the North Sea. They have undertaken trials on tank models using a design

based on proven large submarine configurations, and as a result were able to produce an overall package that may go some way to providing military and commercial markets with the vehicle that could fulfil their requirements. The task of the design team was to utilize off-the-shelf components wherever possible, to ensure proven reliability and keep costs to an acceptable level. The research and development team pin-pointed two configurations for possible development: the first was the Deep-Discharge Lead-Acid Battery propulsion power unit, the second is the Closed-Circuit Energy Source Propulsion Power Unit.

The advanced concept Deep-Discharge Lead-Acid Battery powered vehicle has the advantages of low cost, least technical risk, low acoustic signature, reduced design complications, and the fact that it utilizes established technology. On the minus side it has a reduced operational capability, requires a large hull, and although the basic design concluded that it could carry the same payload at the same speed, it has an operational range of only 100 nautical miles.

The Closed-Cycle Energy Source (CCES) powered vehicle offers the advantages of a very high energy/density unit and was the smallest and lightest of the proposed designs. It could operate to a range of 300 nautical miles, carrying the required payload. The disadvantages are that although the engine is established technology, it is not in production, and there are technical risks.

These are just some of the many problems which face small submarine designers and operators, and it will not become easier. Research funding has in the past been forthcoming from defence industries, but with the dramatic decline in military requirements, budgets have diminished and that has placed the burden of funding on to commercial and research organizations. That may result in a decline in small submarine development.

Chapter 9

Remote Operated Vehicles

IN THE MID-1970s, saturation divers were the key element in all underwater work tasks, but their domination was to be drastically reduced by the introduction of a new partner – Remotely Operated Vehicles (ROVs). It was an uneasy partnership and one built on mistrust, because the divers perceived the new vehicles as threatening to take over work traditionally done by them. ROV operators at that time did nothing to dispel these fears, and instead promoted the virtues of the vehicles far beyond their capabilities. In fact the reliability of those early vehicles was such that divers spent a considerable amount of their time recovering them.

The greatest problem that has been encountered by all ROV designers, manufactures and operators is the environment in which the vehicles have to operate. Placing electrical, electronic or mechanical systems underwater is very difficult, for the two are alien and do not mix. This is not helped by the fact that the launch and recovery methods for the early vehicles were via their umbilicals, and if they were damaged, non-operational time was needed to effect repairs. All of these vehicles have been, and are, weather-dependent. It makes a difference if the vehicle is located on an offshore structure, for that provides a stable deployment platform and only the actual sea state has to be considered. If the vehicle is deployed from a vessel, then the movement of the vessel as well as the sea state will have an adverse effect on all aspects of its operations. This is a particular problem today, when many work programmes utilize vessels such as small survey ships which are not designed for operating with boxes of

electronic technology.

An ROV requires a control system that will enable it to carry out work functions, and that control is provided through an umbilical that enables a power signal and data to be transmitted between the control unit and the vehicle. An operator 'flies' an ROV in a way similar to a helicopter, for it can move in all planes and has the ability to hover. However, in contrast to a helicopter pilot, who can 'feel' his or her surrounding conditions, the ROV pilot has to rely on a television monitor for positioning, and from that adjust the vehicle's direction and power thrust to remain in position. Added to the problems of vehicle stability, which may be enhanced if working close to the surface of the water, is the drag factor on the umbilical.

Skill on the part of the ROV pilot will allow the vehicle to be flown, but another factor that affects all underwater operations is water clarity. Suspended matter can restrict visibility, and vehicles operating at or near the seabed can stir up material themselves which, if it is silty, will reduce the visibility to zero. The pilot is then faced with the twin problems of getting lost, and of fouling the umbilical on an underwater obstruction.

The early vehicle developments were generally limited to the introduction of television cameras, but clients wanted the vehicles to become larger and more powerful and include the addition of manipulators to undertake certain tasks. Technology for operational ROVs still requires them to have a physical link to the surface, and this is achieved through umbilical tether management systems. The development of underwater robots, which do not require umbilicals, is described elsewhere in this book (see the next chapter), but that technology is not yet suitable for other than open water survey work. The working equipment on the larger modern vehicles requires an umbilical to provide the power supply and control functions, but the more functions that are required, the larger the umbilical will be, which in turn creates handling problems when underwater.

One option that is available to help overcome these problems is to split the physical link into two parts. The first part is an umbilical mounted on a winch located on the surface support vessel or structure. This umbilical is armoured and is able to lift the vehicle when it is out of the water. A crane or gantry enables the vehicle to be lifted up and over the side, so that it can be lowered into the water. The umbilical is made up of all the cables that are required to operate the vehicle and is used to lower the vehicle to depth. It remains hanging in the vertical position below the launch point. The second part of the deployment system is located underwater and is the tether management system. One end of the umbilical is connected to a submersible winch, the other to the ROV. The winch holds a tether of

some 183 m (600 ft) which is paid out when operating underwater, allowing the vehicle a circle of that radius in which to work while keeping the drag factor on the tether to a minimum.

Another problem that faced ROV designers and operators was how to hold the vehicles stable so that the manipulator and other systems could be operated successfully. One of the most effective solutions has been a dynamic position system

The Rigworker is an ROV which has evolved through the years to take over many of the operations previously done by the diver. It can work at depths up to 915 m (3,000 ft) and can be fitted with two manipulators and a wide range of equipment packages. (Offshore Systems Engineering Ltd)

A Rigworker ROV and transportable waverider deployment system in the ready-to-launch position. The vehicle is equipped with colour television cameras, manipulator and electronic inspection equipment, which will allow it to undertake detailed inspection programmes of offshore structures. (Rockwater)

combined with a suction device. A rubber suction pad is fitted to the end of the ROV's hydraulic arm. The vehicle is flown to the required location and the suction pad is placed against the structure. A pump is activated to draw out the water from the area within the pad and thus cause a suction. When the vehicle has been attached to the platform in this manner, it has a fixed datum point which is fed into the vehicle's operating system. The vehicle's sensors calculate any movement in the sea caused by wave motion or current and operate the vehicle's thruster to counter the movement. The advantages with this method of attachment are that it cannot cause any damage to the structure, and if the vehicle has to be moved rapidly, the suction just has to be released and the vehicle can move off.

Another method of attachment that has become popular is a manipulator-type grab. This allows the vehicle to approach a structure with the grab sections open and the hydraulic arm extended. Once in place, the grab sections are closed, completing a grip. To move the vehicle, the grab sections are simply opened, freeing the vehicle from the structure.

Deploying a vehicle underwater and

being able to 'fly' it and secure it in one location is only one aspect of the overall concept. To be financially viable, the vehicle has to be able to perform work functions while underwater. The most basic ROVs carry television cameras and relay either black and white or colour pictures to the surface. These same cameras are used by the pilot for navigation purposes. The real 'work' is said to be undertaken when using manipulators, of which one or two can be fitted to the vehicle. There has been an advance in recent years in the development of manipulators, which range from a basic three-function device to a sophisticated nine-function unit with a dexterity that is almost human. Most vehicles are designed as a basic vehicle with add-on facilities, allowing manipulators or special tools to be fitted depending upon the work task.

For most operational purposes the mid-point function capability is acceptable. For general construction and maintenance-type work where tools such as rotary wire brushes, grinding or cutting disks, rigging, impact wrenches or high-pressure water jets are being used, a more heavy-duty, five-function manipulator would be adequate. Where greater dexter-

The Triton ROV entered the market in 1985 and has been uprated through the years. Able to operate at 1,000 m (3,281 ft), it can be equipped with two manipulators, sonar units, cameras, survey and bathymetric suites and numerous hydraulic tools. (Perry Tritech)

ity is required for close-up inspection, the placing of specialist inspection probes or measuring devices, then a seven-function unit would prove to be more flexible. These can be operated by the operator wearing a glove-type device on the hands which transmits signals to the manipulator, telling it to emulate the operator's hand and finger movements.

The ROV's thrusters, manipulators and sensor equipment are controlled by a pilot who sits at a control console sited on the vehicle launch platform at the surface. Television cameras relay pictures to monitors and provide a visual reference. Sonar and gyro compass and navigation are provided and are a vital function, as accurate knowledge of the vehicle's exact whereabouts and status at any given time is essential. The pilot has a joystick for vehicle direction control, but a major disadvantage is the lack of 'feel' of the vehicle's movements. In murky underwater conditions he has to rely exclusively on his instruments to enable him to operate the vehicle.

In and around sub-sea structures, the pilot relies on his television monitors, which offer a fairly narrow field of vision, although most cameras are mounted on a pan and tilt system which, as the name implies, allows the camera angle to be raised or lowered and moved from side to side. One frequent problem is that the vehicle's umbilical or tether becomes fouled. This means that the pilot has to retrace the vehicle's course and locate the source and nature of the problem. A major reason for concern is often found at remote underwater structures. They attract fish, which in turn attract fishermen whose nets snag on the structures and are torn and dumped there. The vehicle undertaking a survey of these structures can become fouled, particularly in water with poor visibility, sometimes to the point where it cannot be retrieved.

Apart from 'flying' the vehicle, the pilot has to operate camera movements, the manipulators and the tether management system. Each work scope that the vehicle is expected to perform will be different, and as a consequence the pilot may well use another member of the team to assist with the handling of the vehicle's systems. Instruments carried on board the vehicle continue to relay to the control console a range of operational information, and during inspection operations a technician will record the data gathered and trans-

NUFO is capable of a forward speed of 3.5 knots and can operate at a depth of 500 m (1,640 ft) with an optional capability down to 1,000 m (3,281 ft). The thrusters can be seen below the electronic pods, and the television cameras and lights adorn the front. (Offshore Systems Engineering Ltd)

mitted by the instruments carried on the vehicle, as well as providing a commentary for the television pictures that are received and recorded on video. Another vital part of the ROV team are the technicians who maintain and repair damaged components and keep the vehicle operational, often a thankless task when expensive rigs, platforms or vessels are waiting for them to undertake a task.

ROV technology began with very modest means. One of the earliest was the *RCV*, which was designed and developed by Hydro Products. It was essentially an observation tool equipped with a television camera which could relay pictures up to the surface. It was a small vehicle and had limited functions compared to the larger vehicles that were to be developed.

The first ROV to be fitted with a micro computer was the *Smartie*, designed and developed by Marine Unit Technology. It was controlled by an operator on the surface who had joysticks which when pushed at a certain angle would provide thrust and move the craft in a given direction. The vehicle was technically very advanced in that the computer accepted input from the magnetic compass and gyro, providing the operator with an artificial target and therefore allowing the vehicle to be flown in nil visibility. It also had a device which would allow it to be placed in one spot and then, by actuating

what could be described as an automatic pilot, maintained in that position. The *Smartie* unit comprised a control console, a launch frame with a winch for the umbilical and a power supply. It was carried to its operating depth in a garage, which had its own tether drum, and there was also a tether between the garage and the vehicle. The vehicle had many problems but it was the design basis for all future small ROVs.

Trov was a much larger vehicle that found its way into the offshore oil industry through the BP subsidiary Sonarmarine Ltd in 1977. The aim was to design and develop the vehicle so that it could become operational in 1975. There was a series of trials and faults which had to be overcome but by 1978 six *Trov*s had been built. *Trov* was basically a large box-shape design measuring 1.52 m (5 ft) x 0.91 m (3 ft) x 1.22 m (4 ft). The vehicle was fitted with two very basic manipulators with such limited ability that one had only 7° of freedom and the other 4°. Also fitted were a television camera, a number of underwater lights, a depth gauge and a gyro compass.

Another vehicle that entered the offshore scene in the same period was the *Trek*. It was of similar proportions to the *Trov* and equally ugly in design. The vehicle came as a package and was encompassed in a large container which had the control console at one end and the vehicle and workshop at the other. It was home for the vehicle when it was not in the water, and it allowed the operators to make repairs and undertake maintenance, of which there was plenty.

A crane lifted the vehicle off the deck and lowered it either over the side or through a moon pool into the sea. The crane wire had a special latch assembly that allowed the vehicle to be lowered to the surface of the sea and then become detached, leaving it connected to its support vessel by its umbilical. The umbilical was paid out manually by additional personnel.

Once in the water, *Trek* was submerged by the pilot who directed the thruster power upwards and so pushed the vehicle down. The television screen gave a view of

The Trek *remote operated vehicle was one of the first to operate in the North Sea. It was basic in design and equipped with black and white television cameras and a very basic manipulator.*

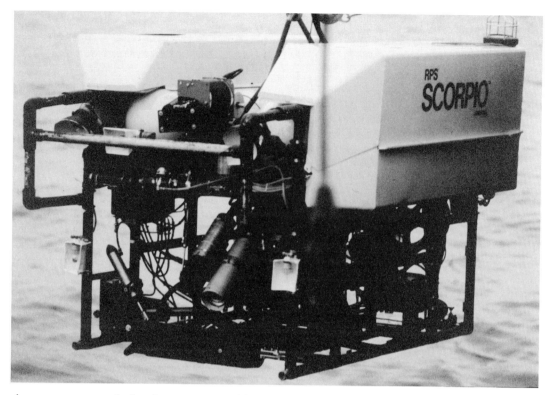

Scorpio has been in service in the North Sea for many years and has been updated as new equipment has evolved. The television camera and lights shown fitted are dated technology and are an example of the equipment that will have been upgraded. Thruster motors are another part of the system which are subject to updating as new models become available.

the compass and depth gauge, enabling the vehicle's direction and depth to be determined. The biggest problem was that the umbilical was heavy and not easily controlled, and it could, and frequently did, get fouled on the numerous protrusions on a platform. It then required divers to be deployed in order to undo the tangle so that it could be recovered.

The electronics were unreliable and usually broke down at the worst possible time, leaving the vehicle trapped or floating upside down on the surface and having to be subjected to an ungainly recovery. However, when these early vehicles did work, they began to prove their worth and could undertake general platform surveys. They were able to 'fly' the outside faces of the platforms' legs and bracings and, by using TV cameras, were able to record any damage and marine growth. The information was recorded on video tape and details noted on drawings. At that period only black and white cameras and videos were in use, giving a rather bland picture and omitting some of the finer details that colour was to offer.

As ROVs became more successful and reliable the offshore oil and gas industry determined that machine should take over

from man, and to that end many of the larger companies began to participate in research programmes, if they were not already involved. The nature of that research was expensive and time-consuming, but competition was both widespread and determined. Vehicles were wanted with greater power, smaller television cameras with the ability to see in low light, and colour television cameras. A large ROV had to be more adaptable than just a mobile television camera platform, and so additional types of equipment were developed.

Buried pipelines needed to be inspected, and this was one case where a vehicle could be deployed to undertake a task that had long been the preserve of the diver. The uprated vehicles could locate and follow a pipeline and, by using the television cameras which extended either side, undertake a single journey along the pipeline while viewing and video recording both sides. Because of the introduction of better navigation systems the exact location of the ROV could be determined by the identification of each of the pipeline's joints, which had numbers painted on them. Damage to a pipeline could be assessed and scour identified (where the seabed under the pipeline had been washed out by the current). All of this could be recorded and plotted so that remedial work could be planned.

Further developments in manipulator design made them more dextrous, and able to undertake more functions. Tools could be made and fitted which would allow the ROVs to undertake specialist tasks. This was a major advance on the early units, which could pick up and retrieve a sample from the seabed; now they could open or close valves.

The small ROV became popular as it could record information onto video. That was of value to engineers, who were able to undertake general visual inspection work much more cheaply than by using a diver. The UFO 225 found a ready market, and many jobs were the recipient of the small yellow 'eyeball', as it became known. Many hours of useful, constructive work have been and continue to be undertaken by these vehicles.

The UFO 300 series had a remote video inspection system fitted which included a Silicon Intensified Target (SIT) camera capable of working in very poor light conditions. The vehicle itself is constructed from synthetic foam plastic, anodized aluminium and stainless steel. The design of

the vehicle allows it to move easily through the water with minimum drag. Four powerful thrusters are mounted inside ducts that have proved to be very good and safe when in close proximity to divers. Because the propellers are inside the ducts they prevent damage and fouling from rope or other debris. To maintain high reliability, the vehicle is comprised of sub-assemblies, which means that bits can be changed easily and quickly, and like the earlier model it is launched from a garage on its own tether.

Some developments took ROVs beyond their initial concept, and one such vehicle was the Platform Inspection Cleaning (PIC), which was designated a medium-sized ROV. The special feature of this vehicle was that it could attach itself to concrete platforms or the steel legs and bracings of platforms either vertically or horizontally. The attachment was achieved by the use of four Wyndac limpets with a powerful suction force. The vehicle was designed to undertake underwater cleaning operations and for that purpose it was fitted with a water jetting system for surface cleaning. Video cameras allowed visual inspection, and other equipment, such as survey equipment, could be fitted. It gave cathodic protection

An RCV 225 ROV and launch system endures rough seas on its deployment vessel. The weather conditions, in particular winter storms, have caused ROV pilots many concerns for the safety of their vehicles. (Rockwater)

readings and had a steel thickness gauge. The overall plan was to develop a vehicle system which could undertake every aspect of underwater inspection and take over from the diver. The PIC vehicle was large and, because of the work functions it was required to undertake, it required a heavy power supply to operate its many tools. The answer was a heavy, large-diameter umbilical which in turn demanded a large powerful winch, and because of its size, the entire system had to be deployed from a large support vessel.

Another large, innovative remote operated vehicle was *David*, a product of Germany, which was designed not only as a conventional ROV but as a diver support vehicle. Powerful thrusters enabled it to be flown to the work site where large hydraulic-powered jaws could grip the legs or bracings of a structure. An added advantage of this jaw system was that it could rotate, which meant that if the attachment brace was at an angle, the vehicle could be maintained on a level plane. The vehicle also addressed the problem of diver stability by providing a dual-purpose ladder and crane. If divers had to use heavy tools they needed something to hang on to or gain a purchase on. In open water this was often very difficult, but the ladder or crane provided a fixed platform so that the diver could secure himself, leaving both hands free to handle tools or equipment.

Extending the diver assistance concept still further, *David* had a hydraulic power system to which tools could be connected. Normally, when a diver working at depth required tools such as an impact wrench, a grinder or a wire brush, they would have to be lowered to him from the support vessel or structure with a power supply hose which could be affected by the current or foul on obstructions. This of course all took time. The advantage with *David* was that it could have the tools fitted before the dive, requiring the diver only to go to the vehicle, take the tool, uncoil a short length of hose and return to work. Other possible additions included a limited duration underwater cutting system or wet welding unit. *David* would have been useful for carrying the under-

water Magnetic Particle Inspection (MPI) unit, which is a heavy and cumbersome item of equipment, but it was large and, at the time of its development, complicated, and these two factors, combined with the cost of purchase or hire, weighed against its use. It was seen as an expensive toy, and so the concept was not developed. Divers today still have tools sent down to them from the surface.

The US Navy developed a range of ROVs for military purposes, one of the most important being the Umbilical Controlled Underwater Recovery Vehicle (CURV), which made its mark and found favour. The improved *CURV II* was an unmanned tethered submersible capable of operating to 1,220 m (4,000 ft) and was the successor to *CURV I*, which recovered the H-bomb off the coast of Spain in 1966.

CURV III has a greater depth capability

David *was a large ROV designed to provide support to divers. Large jaws enabled the vehicle to attach itself to a structure. It also had a ladder crane which offered divers a platform where they could secure themselves, leaving their hands free to work. The disadvantage of a vehicle of this size and power was the size of the umbilical and handling system needed.*

CURV I, II and III *were the US Navy's underwater recovery vehicles, each one an update of the previous vehicle. The Mk II had a depth capability of 1,220 m (4,000 ft) and is shown here equipped with a seven-function tool arm which can be fitted with a grasping claw, cable cutters and modified tools. Its successor, CURV III, was used in the rescue of the manned* Pisces III *submersible which sank in 1973 in the Atlantic off the south-west coast of Eire.* (US Navy)

than *CURV II*, being designed to operate to depths of 2,134 m (7,000 ft) at a submerged speed of 4 knots. It has been modified to operate in emergencies to a depth of 3,048 m (10,000 ft). The *CURV III* system consists of the vehicle, the umbilical and the control console. Although it often operates from a dedicated surface support vessel, the system is designed so that all major operational components can be disassembled, air transported to a work site, and installed on any suitable surface vessel with adequate deck space. The vehicle normally carries a hydraulically operated claw for attaching and recovering objects from the seabed. For special tasks, the claw can be removed and replaced by a variety of grasping, cutting or working tools.

The vehicle contains all the necessary equipment for searching, locating and documenting the lost item. Control of the vehicle and monitoring of operations are performed in the control van where the

pilot utilizes the vehicle's onboard instrument packages which include a straza 500 active/passive sonar with transponder interrogation capability, acoustic altimeter, a depth meter, compass, two television cameras with lights, and a 35mm still camera and strobe light. It is a versatile underwater vehicle which can be readily modified to accommodate a wide variety of underwater tasks, and it has adequately demonstrated its search and recovery capabilities, most notably during the 1973 rescue of the *Pisces III* submersible off Ireland, which is described in Chapter 8 of this book.

For years Dr Robert Ballard had dreamed of developing unmanned underwater vehicles that could be deployed into the deep oceans in order to use video and still cameras to record events and findings. He had explored the ocean depths in *Alvin*, the Woods Hole Oceanographic Institute's (WHOI) manned submersible, but had experienced some of the restrictions of a manned craft. To develop underwater vehicles requires considerable funding, because apart from the vehicle there is a need for underwater cameras, navigation and control systems. Once the funding has been obtained there is the question of a trials and test project. Robert Ballard had that in mind as well, knowing that his plan, if successful, would be one of the most dramatic underwater expeditions ever mounted. He would find, and capture on video, the wreck of the *Titanic*.

On the night of 14–15 April 1912, the R.M.S. *Titanic* struck an iceberg in the North Atlantic and became the world's worst shipping disaster. The *Titanic* was the largest and most luxurious liner of its time, and on the night disaster struck, she was on her maiden voyage. The second ship of an intended trio, *Titanic* was sister to the *Olympic*, which was only slightly smaller. She was the pride of the fleet, and was thought to be unsinkable. As part of the White Star Line, these ships were built to offer pure comfort and luxury, especially to first-class passengers.

It was 10 April 1912 when, under a hail of publicity, the ship sailed from Southampton bound for New York. There were 1,316 passengers, including both millionaires and poor immigrants, 885 officers and crew on board, a total of 2,201 persons, though ironically the Board of Trade only required *Titanic* to carry 20 lifeboats, with a total capacity for only 1,178 persons. The impact with the iceberg tore a 91.5 m (300 ft) gash in the ship's side below the waterline. The resulting flooding caused her to sink in 2 hours 40 minutes. Of the 2,201 persons on board, only 712 were to survive.

Funding for Robert Ballard's project came from the US Navy and support was provided by Woods Hole, so in 1980 the design and construction of an underwater vehicle began. Two vehicles were developed: one was a remote controlled deep-towed sled which carried video cameras and electronic equipment, the other was to be carried by the first vehicle and would have its own propulsion system that would enable it to carry a video camera and get close to an object.

The dream became a reality with *Argo* and *Jason*. Ballard chose these names as a reference to Jason and his mythological ship *Argo*, which sailed in search of the Golden Fleece in the ancient Greek legend.

Argo is an unmanned submersible which is connected to the surface support ship by a combined umbilical and tow cable. It does not have any form of independent propulsion system but relies on being towed. It carries a variety of cameras, both video and still, and sonar systems that can search forwards and sideways to seek out targets for avoidance and investigation. *Jason* is an independent remote operated vehicle with its own propulsion system and management which can be flown to the extent of its tether to investigate and video at close quarters all manner of objects.

By 1983 *Argo* was becoming a reality but *Jason* was still on the drawing board. The pressure increased to test the *Argo* system, which would take Robert Ballard one step closer to finding the *Titanic*. The full story of Robert Ballard's endeavours are described in his book *Discovery of the Titanic*. *Argo* was used in the 1985 expedition and brought the first pictures of the wreck of the *Titanic* lying on the ocean floor at a depth of 3,800 m (12,460 ft). While armchair adventurers could sit and watch on their televisions the dramatic pictures of the outside of the ship, Robert Ballard wanted to take the search further and explore inside the wreck. That would require a remote operated vehicle.

A year later, again supported by Woods Hole and funded by the US Navy, Robert Ballard returned to the location of the *Titanic*. This time he had the manned submersible *Alvin*, which was adapted to carry a small remote operated vehicle, *Jason Junior*, or, as it was to become known, *JJ*. The vehicle had a special cage on the front of *Alvin* and was connected by a 76.26 m (250 ft) tether. It had its own propulsion system, carried colour video cameras and was controlled from within *Alvin*. *JJ*'s size meant that it would be able to enter the *Titanic* through broken windows and doors and go where a larger vehicle could not.

The support vessel *Atlantis II* was home

for *Alvin*, *JJ* and the expedition team, but one problem faced the expedition. *Alvin* had no back-up in an emergency and if the submersible became trapped and could not free itself, there was little hope of rescue. The answer was to take *Alvin* to safe locations and let *JJ* take the risks. If the ROV became trapped a cable cutter on the vehicle's carrying cage could cut the tether, leaving *Alvin* free of entanglement.

Alvin was fitted with a black and white camera at the front for navigation purposes, while a colour camera was fitted to the manipulator arm which could be moved within the limitations of the arm. Both of these cameras were connected to video recorders which were operated continously throughout the dive. *JJ* was operated by a member of the submersible's crew of three, who also controlled thrust movement and activated the 35mm still camera which was sited alongside the colour video camera. This camera also had a video recorder inside the submersible, which together with the crew made for very cramped conditions.

The key to the success of this expedition was *JJ*, which has shown a very wide audience the advantages to be obtained from a remote operated vehicle. While *Alvin* sat on the upper deck of the *Titanic*, *JJ* was flown into the ship and descended amongst the once elegant surroundings. The once grand staircase and balconies had been subjected to an alien environment for many years and the results were clear to see. It required great skill on the part of *JJ*'s operators to fly the vehicle in and out of rooms, along passages and down stairways. At any time the tether could have become fouled, trapping the vehicle. When a section of the ship had been explored, *JJ* would return to its carrying cage and *Alvin* would be moved to another location, and the exploring process would begin again. The results of the expedition are widely available in video and still pictures, provided by ROV and underwater electronic technology.

There is now a new breed of 'package' vehicles such as the Multi-Role Vehicle (MRV), which is not a single vehicle but a combination of different vehicles achieved through a system of add-on modules. The modules can be survey packages or specifically designed tool skids which will meet a particular company's requirements. As companies explore into deeper water and install seabed structures, they are looking to replace the diver by designing the subsea unit so that an ROV can gain access to the working parts, and those working parts are designed so that an ROV tool package can undertake maintenance or replacement.

Advanced technology is now being applied to untethered, free-swimming undersea vehicles and is the subject of a separate chapter (Chapter 11). It is however evident that while relatively shallow operations to 3,048 m (10,000 ft) can be efficiently accomplished by tethered vehicles with their unlimited power availability and immediate operator monitor and control, untethered vehicles offer advantages. They can utilize a smaller support ship since cable handling and storage is not required, nor do they require the support ship to maintain rigid station keeping. The untethered vehicle does not require excessive thrust to tow a cable and can run long manoeuvres without concern for surface support. The primary goal of undersea technological advances in microprocessors, sensors, data links, voice-actuated manipulators and tools is to build a system that, when given the decision and control logic of artificial intelligence, can perform a multitude of undersea tasks.

The exploitation of the world's oceans for mineral resources and scientific research has created a demand for more sophisticated ROVs, in many cases to undertake work tasks that normally would have been the domain of the diver. The cost of an ROV package measured against a saturation diving package weighs heavily in favour of the ROV. That said, ROVs will never, at least for the foreseeable future, replace the diver, but they will certainly encroach deeply into the sphere of operations that has hitherto been that of the diver, both in shallow and in deep water.

Chapter 10

Underwater Robots

ROBOT VEHICLES HAVE been technically possible for quite some time, but their usefulness was severely restricted by inadequate technology. However, in the mid-1970s technological advances started to transform this situation. In France, an underwater vehicle, the *Epaulard*, was developed in 1977 by IFREMER and ECA. It was unmanned and had no physical link with the surface, and after production, began trials in 1979. For its initial dives it was tethered to the mother vessel to ensure that the onboard computers and navigation systems worked correctly. The vehicle was fairly small and therefore its range and payload were restricted, but it proved the system and further developments have taken place since.

Epaulard required a surface support ship with the ability to launch and recover the vehicle, and to carry the operations team of four or five people. In support terms, therefore, it was very cost-effective. Trials and operational dives were successful and the vehicle accomplished 130 dives, covered some 8.5 km (5 miles) and took over 200,000 detailed photographs of the seabed. Using its obstacle avoidance sonar it located and identified objects in water depths of up to 1,280 m (4,200 ft). Initially, the vehicle was controlled through an umbilical, but it was soon proved to be reliable and control was transferred to through-water acoustic transmissions between the surface support vessel and the vehicle.

Epaulard's success began in 1981 when, following extensive trials, it carried out its first operational dive and proved its operational capability by surveying 30–50 km (18.5–31 miles) of seabed a day while undertaking a full photographic coverage. The navigation system proved to be accurate to within 2 per cent of the water depth and the launch and recovery operation could be accomplished in weather conditions up to sea state 4.

The vehicle could descend to 6,000 m (19,686 ft) and remain operational for up to eight hours while travelling at a speed of up to 1 m per second (3 ft/sec). It was equipped with a Benthos 377 vertically mounted still camera which took

The Epaulard *was the first unmanned, entirely autonomous submersible with the ability to dive and operate at 6,000 m (19,686 ft). It can undertake photographic and bathymetric surveys of the deep ocean seabed. It navigates through the water and at a preset height over the seabed. (Société ECA)*

Figure 14: *The* Epaulard *system as developed by the Centre National d'Eploitation des Océans (CNXO). The ECA company was a prime contractor. The* Epaulard *was the first unmanned, entirely autonomous submersible, and could dive to 6,000 m (19,686 ft) and remain submerged for several hours. It navigated at a constant altitude over the seabed, and was monitored by means of acoustic commands and tracked by an ultrashort base system.*

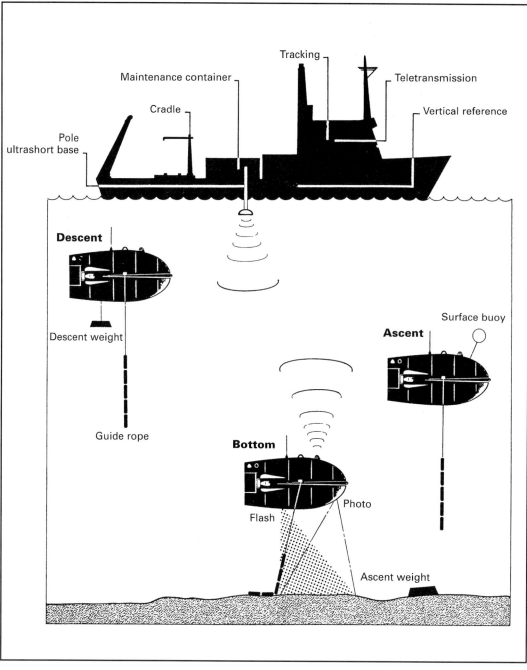

3,000–5,000 photographs at periods of 5–10 seconds. The time, course, altitude and depth were displayed on each photograph, which is critical for survey purposes. There was no through-water transmission for film, so if an object was recorded, there needed to be a system for locating it again.

The heart of the vehicle was the control system, three microprocessors that transmitted the submersible's course, battery voltage and altitude to the support vessel.

The vehicle's course could be changed acoustically by signals transmitted from the control room on the support vessel. Upon completion of a dive, the vehicle released an ascent weight which dropped to the seabed, allowing it to return to the surface. The vehicle was then recovered by the support ship, to undergo maintenance and preparation for the next dive. The valuable film was removed from the camera and processed, and the information it recorded studied in detail.

By 1985 *Epaulard* had completed 130 dives, covered more than 850 km (528 miles) and taken more than 200,000 photographs, providing considerable details of the seabed. Two of the most important operations undertaken by the vehicle took place in US waters in 1983. The Deep Ocean research project was undertaken in Coos Bay, Oregon, in the area known as Gorda Rift and the Juan de Fuca Ridge. The technology used in the design and development of *Epaulard* allowed the vehicle to operate without an umbilical to the surface in order to survey and photograph large areas of seabed. For this operation the vehicle would 'fly' through an area of valleys and cavernous cliff-type terrain. This gave rise to concern among the operations team, because if the vehicle entered a cave they would not be able to recover it. Nevertheless the operation went ahead, with the result that more than 15,000 photographs were taken over the five-day period.

The US Navy were interested in *Epaulard*'s technology and consequently employed it to locate and photograph a Second World War Douglas Dauntless bomber in 1,280 m (4,200 ft) of water. The vehicle was pre-programmed to follow a search grid covering 7.77 sq km (3 sq miles) of seabed. It was launched and descended to a point just above the seabed and began its search at the start point using the onboard sonar. The grid pattern was followed automatically until the wreck of the aircraft was located. The surface command system regained control of the vehicle and directed it to circle the wreck and take photographs. Back on board the support vessel, the photographs were processed and provided the US Navy with visual evidence of their aircraft.

Scicon, a British company, looked at the available technology and possible future developments of underwater vehicles and came up with an underwater robot system which they named *Spur*. It was based upon a military concept of a small unmanned attack robot submarine, but with a view to commercial applications as well.

With a length of 10 m (33 ft) and width and height of 1.8 m (6 ft), it was of a streamlined design with speed in mind and as a result had a cruising speed of 12

The Spur *is an autonomous submersible fitted with computers that can be pre-programmed to undertake deep ocean survey work. The original concept was for a cost-effective unmanned military submarine, but with the rapid development of deep ocean robotic vehicles, the* Spur *could have commercial applications.* (Scicon)

knots and a top speed of 50 knots. The radius of operation at cruising speed was 1,000 nautical miles, which could be enhanced to 2,000 nautical miles with the addition of drop tanks. It was capable of diving to depths of 6,000 m (19,686 ft), and this could be increased by modifying the design. Because it was designed for military operations, communications with the vehicles would be by ELF, EHF and possibly blue laser, along with the use of special aerials and buoys if necessary. Mock-ups of the vehicle were constructed, and the electronic and computer technology was available, but it did not reach the experimental stage for either military or commercial applications.

The Institute of Oceanographic Sciences, Deacon Laboratory (IOSDL) is the UK leader in deep ocean research. They have a proven record for innovation and research in marine technology, particularly in deep ocean survey. One major development has been in the design of side scan sonars, the most famous of which is 'Gloria', with its long-range acoustic images of the deep ocean floor. Another innovation is the 'TOBI' (Towed Ocean Bottom Instrument) system, which has a powerful side scan sonar that allows scientists to zoom in on seabed targets that have been identified by 'Gloria' and produce results that compare favourably with shallow water systems.

'TOBI' is a deep-towed, flexible instrument platform that has the advantage of excellent stability. It can operate down to depths of 6,000 m (19,686 ft) where it can identify items only 2 m (6 ft 6 in) across. This makes very accurate deep ocean profiling possible. As with most underwater developments, the system is very versatile, and its instrument packages can offer support or research to a wide range of applications, including hydrocarbon exploration, marine mining surveys, hazard mapping, cable and pipeline routeing through critical areas, and marine salvage. It weighs 2 tonnes in air but once in the water is neutrally buoyant through the addition of syntactic foam. The construction of the unit is based upon an open-frame concept that allows the addition of extra instrument packages to meet a pro-

ject's or client's specific requirements to a total payload capacity of 400 kg (882 lb). The basic system has a dual side scan sonar, sub-bottom profiles and a magnetometer in addition to the vehicle's control and function systems.

The towed unit consists of two parts, a depressor weight and the main system. The 600 kg (1,323 lb) depressor weight is attached to a steel towing cable and the vehicle is attached to the depressor by 200 m (656 ft) of umbilical rope, which makes the whole system stable, even in high sea states. During towing operations the wire has to be kept at a pre-determined length so that an altitude of between 300 and 400 m (984–1,312 ft) above the seabed can be maintained.

The umbilical carries data from the instrument packages on the vehicle to monitors in the control van on the surface support vessel. That data is collected from the two side scan systems (which have been corrected for geometric distortion) before being displayed on both a high-resolution monitor and a thermal paper recorder. Data from the sub-bottom profiler is displayed on to a linescan recorder to reveal sub-bottom reflections, while other sensors relay information to the surface which is displayed in digital form on monitors. All of the data received from the vehicle is stored on a retrieval system so that more detailed analysis can be undertaken by scientists and technicians when the survey is completed and they are ashore and have analytical equipment available.

To gain vital knowledge of the oceans, IOSDL has developed a wide range of underwater instruments including the bathysnap. This is a time-lapse camera system that is deployed on the seabed to gather a pictorial record. The Underwater Camera System is a self-contained time-lapse camera which can operate for up to 400 days at full ocean depth. Apart from surveys of the seabed, other ocean research is undertaken using systems such as the Multiple Rectangular Mid-water Trawl, which are acoustically controlled plankton and micronekton nets. The Institute has more than 40 years' experience in sonar research and has developed a range of successful side scan and profile sonars, all of which provide researchers, scientists and engineers with vital information.

'DOGGIE' and 'DOLPHIN'

Much of what scientists want to know about the seabed of our oceans and seas is already crudely known. Decades of echo-sounding have established its approximate shape and highlighted the main features of the topography. Using side-scanning sonars, researchers have established the fabric or texture of the seabed, which means that it is roughly known where gigantic submarine landslides have occurred, and where bottom currents have scoured out craters.

Most of what is known about the shape and texture of the deep ocean seabed, as well as its magnetic character and the disposition of underlying structures, has been observed and recorded from instruments deployed at the sea's surface. This view of the oceans can be taken from as much as 5 km (3 miles) up, and is consequently rather fuzzy. To answer all the probing questions about the nature and formation of the seabed and the processes that shape it, we need to take a closer and much more detailed look. This requires a vehicle system that can submerge even in the deep oceans. Because of the vast expanses involved, the vehicle needs to be able to cover the seabed at speeds of 5–6 knots, scanning areas as wide as 5–6 km (3–3½ miles) with side scan sonars and other instruments.

A deep-towed vehicle like the IOSDL 'TOBI' was developed to be towed at a height of 200–300 m (124–186 ft) above the seabed, but towed vehicles are subject to drag and are difficult to manoeuvre when conducting grid surveys. The answer was to develop further, vehicles which did not require towing but were autonomous. The answer was provided in the production of the 'DOGGIE' and 'DOLPHIN' systems.

'DOGGIE' has the advantage not only of tripling the rate of coverage of the seabed but also of freeing the ship from the survey process. While 'DOGGIE' is performing a survey on a predetermined grid, the mother ship can be at another location carrying out other tasks, such as collecting samples or undertaking a more detailed study of selected sites within an area previously surveyed.

The vehicles can be particularly useful for highly detailed studies of relatively small areas of seabed, on topics such as the hydrothermal vent fields associated with ore deposits within the 50 km (31 miles) wide median valleys of mid-ocean ridges. Being designed as a multi-sensor vehicle carrying side scan sonars, a sub-bottom profiler, magnetometer and chemical sensors, a 'DOGGIE' vehicle is capable of providing a wealth of closely related data on the geophysical and geological properties of particular areas of the seabed at all depths.

Of particular interest is the eventual possibility of using the vehicles to survey under ice. Ice-covered seas present the ocean research bodies with a remarkable challenge for deep ocean cartography, because at present these areas are only surveyed in any detail by military submarines, and much of the information they collect is classified. The benefits to geologists and geophysicists from such a technology would be considerable, as currently it is impossible to answer many of the questions we have about what shapes the deep oceans' seabed. The main lack has been a ready means of obtaining high-resolution image data, for what is needed is detailed images of the deep oceans. Without knowledge of the processes that shape the deep seabed, there will be a failure to appreciate how it may be used or in what ways it may change in the future.

The development during the 1990s of another system, called 'DOLPHIN', represents an ideal way of automating wide-area hydrographic data-gathering throughout the deep oceans and under ice. By conducting complete deep water sections across ocean basins, 'DOLPHIN' could provide the natural complement to satellite observations of the surface, to fixed moorings at selected locations and to the use of other instruments to monitor the mixed layer of the upper ocean and coastal seas.

This Deep Ocean Long Path Hydrographic Instrument ('DOLPHIN') will carry out profiles of the ocean from the surface to the seabed, surfacing every 30 km (18 1/2 miles) to fix its position by Global Positioning Satellite (GPS) and to return data to shore stations. It is estimated that the North Atlantic heat flux, which is vital for maintaining the mild climate of Britain and Europe, could be monitored and possibly redirected by using data from ten trans-ocean 'DOLPHIN' sections carried out routinely several times a year.

In broad terms, improved spatial and temporal sampling of the upper oceans will determine the varying distributions of heat and fresh water, carbon dioxide content, air–sea fluxes, plankton distribution and nutrients. Long-term deep ocean measurements are needed to determine the state of ocean circulation, deep water formation, convection, ventilation and carbon dioxide content. Satellite observations of the ocean will provide data on surface temperature, wind, waves, topography, precipitation, sea-ice concentration and thickness, and chlorophyll content. When assimilated into four-dimensional models, this complete set of measurements, with sufficient accuracy and resolution, would permit computation of the global transport of heat and moisture by oceans, predicting the natural variability of these processes and shedding light on their inter-annual and inter-decadal changes.

Although deep-diving manned and unmanned submersibles have now been in existence for some time, the uniqueness of the 'DOLPHIN' and 'DOGGIE' concepts lies in the combination of capabilities required for operational requirements to be fully met. The development of 'DOLPHIN' required the provision of adequate energy storage for transoceanic passage within a vehicle small enough and light enough to permit handling at sea by ships of modest size. The vehicle needed to be able to dive repeatedly to full ocean depth of 6,000 m (19,686 ft) with minimum energy consumption and with the assurance that it would maintain its operational integrity throughout the many dive and surface cycles. This in turn required

the vehicle to be reliable in its autonomy.

Research and development on autonomous vehicles has been going on for a number of years, but there still remain critical technological concerns for the development of a precise self-navigation system which will work for periods of submergence lasting several days. The vehicle also needs an onboard decision-making capability for ocean floor terrain following, collision avoidance and self-navigation.

The design and development of such a vehicle and all its components were concentrated on the *Autosub* project. This vehicle comprises three main structural components: the pressure hull, containing energy supplies and major elements of the operational management system; a forward section, containing a surfacing buoyancy system, telemetry and collision avoidance subsystems; and a rear section occupied by propulsion units and control elements. Passive buoyancy capsules are distributed at either end of the pressure hull and space will be available for the science payload in fore and aft sections.

The propulsion unit represents the largest single power drain in the vehicle, so an efficient design was particularly important. Failure to achieve expected efficiency increases the energy required for a given operation, which in turn reduces the scope for the science payload. The unit must also operate reliably throughout repeated surfacing and submerging cycles to increased pressures of depth when underwater, so the development and testing of a suitable propulsion unit became a significant part of the *Autosub* project.

Acoustic communication through the ocean can achieve moderate data rates over a range of about 10 km (6 miles), while radio waves will only penetrate a few metres into water. This means that for periods of several hours, while *Autosub* is submerged, there can be no communication between the operator on the surface support vessel and the vehicle. During this time it would have to navigate, control its own flight path, avoid obstacles and manage data acquisition entirely autonomously. When surfaced, there may be an opportunity to establish two-way communication with the operator, allowing the vehicle to telemeter engineering status reports, and if necessary receive fresh operational programmes. The onboard Global Positioning System (GPS) receiver will update the navigation to an accuracy of a few metres.

The Mission Management System (MMS) is the computer system that will control the vehicle while it is deep under the ocean, and the challenge lies in making this system sufficiently reliable. Duplication of parts of the hardware could in theory substantially improve the reliability of the whole system, but would add to the overall size and weight of the vehicle.

All substances are compressible to some degree and furthermore their compression characteristics may change significantly with both pressure and temperature. Sea water exhibits a compression of roughly 2.8 per cent between the surface and a depth of 6,000 m (19,686 ft). Solid substances are usually rather less compressible than this: steel, for example, has approximately 1/70 of the compressibility of sea water. Consequently, solid materials, particularly metals, will appear to decrease in weight and therefore increase their buoyancy with increased depth of immersion in sea water. A pressure hull may, on the other hand, show either an increase or a decrease in buoyancy with depth of immersion in sea water depending upon its structural strength and flexibility.

Autosub will be equipped with a pressure hull that occupies a large proportion of its displaced volume. This is necessary in order to accommodate a large energy source and to help make the vehicle neutrally buoyant at the surface. It would seem unlikely from the results of the IOSDL's research undertaken so far that the pressure hull will also provide sufficient compressibility to counteract the effect of the increased buoyancy of other solid components of the vehicle while retaining adequate strength to resist collapse at full ocean depth.

The combination of strength and lightness is important for the whole vehicle structure and fibre-reinforced plastic (FRP) materials are being studied for possible use. The pressure hull, comprising a circular cylinder with hemispherical end closures, is a particularly important structural component in this respect, requiring a considerable amount of work in the design of a composite pressure hull.

While these research and operational projects have and are being undertaken by the Institute of Oceanographic Sciences (IOSDL) in the UK, William V. Broad interviewed scientists in the USA to compile his report for the 'Science Times' column in the *New York Times* which he aptly titled 'Into the Abyss: New Robots of the Deep'. He provides an interesting perspective on the subject and his article, dated 9 March 1993, is quoted in full:

Undersea robots, which over the decades have opened new realms of activity for the world's navies, oil companies and wreck salvors, are now advancing on their greatest challenge yet. Highly computerised and sometimes free of human control, they are starting to scrutinise the ocean depths on behalf of basic science, promising to deliver a treasure trove of data from the planet's last, largest and most mysterious frontier.

Dozens of deep diving robots are being built or run today by the world's top centres of oceanographic research. Robots cost far less than manned submersibles, are safer, and can stay down far longer amid the darkness, miles beneath the ocean's surface.

Low cost in theory means large numbers. In coming decades, scientists say, hundreds of robots cruising the seas could gather abundant data at a time when the world's oceans will increasingly be threatened by human activity.

'It's the way of the future,' said Dr Charles D. Hollister, a senior scientist at the Woods Hole Oceanographic Institution on Cape Cod, Mass, which is building more than a half dozen different kinds of undersea robots.

Dr Paul J. Fox, an oceanographer at the University of Rhode Island, said the implications were enormous. 'The abyss is the last frontier on this planet,' he said. 'We know almost nothing about it. These remote tools have the potential to synoptically explore, study and characterise its proper-

ties, whether biologic, geologic or chemical. We're on the threshold of a new era.'

Robots are seen as crucial for such jobs as finding the millions of undiscovered life forms thought to inhabit the deep ocean, learning how the planet's water affects the climate, studying the eruption of undersea vents and volcanoes and surveying thousands of miles of coastlines and coral reefs.

They could also police toxic sites. For instance, robots could sound an alarm if radiation started to leak from abandoned nuclear warheads and submarine reactors, some 75 of which are now on the ocean floor.

Two robotic tests going on thousands of miles apart illustrate the field's progress and promise for the future. Explorers from Woods Hole are sending a 2.1 metre (7 foot) long robot named Jason more than 1.6 kilometres (1 mile) down to the bottom of the Gulf of California between the Mexican mainland and Baja California, to study hot vents in the ocean floor and associated life forms. Jason works on a long tether tied to a surface ship. Almost instantly, by way of satellite and the computer network known as INTERNET, its data are flashed around the globe to marine scientists at more than a dozen universities and research institutes.

'This is the most complicated thing I've ever done,' Dr Robert D. Ballard, the expedition's leader and the discoverer of the wreck of the Titanic, last week told more than a half million school children learning about the two week study in a satellite television broadcast.

Some 4800 kilometres (3,000 miles) eastward, off Bermuda in the Atlantic, another Woods Hole team this week is inaugurating a new robot known as ABE, for Autonomous Benthic Explorer. Unlike Jason, it has no tether. An advanced computer system in the vehicle guides it through pre-programmed paces. The vehicle is designed to travel to depths of nearly 6.4 kilometres (4 miles) and to stay there, examining a particular site or region, for up to a year. It can be called back to the surface by an acoustic signal from a ship.

Among its possible jobs would be scrutinising nuclear relics of the Cold War. 'Let's say you've got a sunken reactor and can't afford to recover it unless it's leaking,' Dr

Albert M. Bradley, one of the robot's designers, said last week before setting sail. 'What you need is a watchdog, a sentry. ABE would be ideal, wandering around with a radiation detector.'

The robot cost $1 million. Jason cost $5 million. Alvin, the path breaking submersible that over the decades has repeatedly carried a crew of three people into the ocean depths, cost about $50 million to build and its operations currently run at about $25,000 a day.

The future, scientists say, belongs to penny-pinching robots, especially self-sufficient ones that require no support ships hovering overhead.

Remarkably, one of the field's pioneers has no formal oceanographic credentials. David Packard, the electronics tycoon of Hewlett-Packard fame, founded the Monterey Bay Aquarium Research Institute in Pacific Grove, California in 1987. In its first year he spent $13 million of his own money to buy the institute a research ship and tethered robot, and over the years went on to provide lavish support for the robotic endeavour. 'He realised that oceanography was still in the 19th century and that great strides could be made in scientific research if modern technology was brought to bear,' said Dr Bruce H. Robinson, the institute's science director.

The institute's robot, built by International Submarine Engineering, of British Columbia, was adapted from a model used by oil companies to erect and inspect offshore platforms and pipelines. In addition to the standard mechanical arm, it was outfitted with cameras, sensors and sampling devices, including suction tubes that can capture different kinds of undersea creatures.

The payoffs have been spectacular, with scores of new organisms discovered and existing ones better understood. The jelly-like mucus often found in standard marine dredges turned out to be delicate food-gathering webs a yard long spun by gelatinous invertebrates called larvaceans.

'We find new species all the time,' Dr Robinson said. 'Most of the work by manned submersibles has been on the ocean floor. But we're working the whole water column, which turns out to have the largest *animal communities on earth. We think a quarter to a third of all the species out there have been overlooked.'*

Nine hundred and fourteen metres (3,000 feet) down, the Monterey Institute recently found the first living examples of Vampyroteuthis infernalis, a deep sea cephalopod that is a modern day representative of an evolutionary precursor to squids and octopi. Its spooky name apparently comes from its love of dark places; it has no fangs. The size of a cantaloupe, it does boast a novel kind of light-producing organ.

In 1991, the robotic action spread as oceanographers at the University of Washington and Dr Ballard's Woods Hole team sailed to the Juan de Fuca ridge, an undersea mountain range some 400 kilometres (250 miles) off the Oregon–Washington coast that has active volcanoes and vents. Clouds of black fluid hot enough to melt lead are rich in minerals that have built chimney-like nozzles up to 35 metres (115 feet) tall. Primitive sulfer-eating bacteria that live off vented chemicals feed a large population of deep-sea creatures that never see a ray of sunlight, including huge clams, mussels and 3 metre (10 foot) long tube worms.

Working more than a kilometre deep over a period of three weeks, the Jason robot mapped the region's geology, studied the odd creatures and explored the huge sulphide chimneys over a region area many miles.

Dr Robert W. Embley, a geophysicist with the National Oceanic and Atmospheric Administration's Pacific Environmental Laboratory in Newport, Oregon, was so impressed that he and a team of Canadian colleagues visited the same ridge last year with a Canadian robot. It succeeded in retrieving biologic and geologic samples from the ridge, a robotic first. 'It's a turning point in data collection,' Dr Embley said. 'The profitability and increased efficiency of robots promise to make remote areas of the world's oceans far more accessible.'

Early this year, scientists at the Massachusetts Institute of Technology took the next step, launching an autonomous seven-foot robot named Odyssey in Antarctic waters. It can dive more than five kilometres (three miles), even though its

parts cost a mere $50,000.

'The basic problem is that you have to count on losing anything you put into the ocean,' said Dr James G. Bellingham, one of Odyssey's designers and head of MIT's Sea Grant Underwater Vehicles Laboratory. 'With a big expensive system, you have to be conservative, and that means you're probably not using it in the most scientifically interesting places. It's a Catch 22. The situation is reversed with low cost systems, which are going to revolutionise the way oceanographers gather data.'

Florida Atlantic University in Boca Raton, Fla, is building two autonomous robots, one based on the Odyssey design and a much larger 6 metre (21 foot) one that looks like a military torpedo. It is being developed in conjunction with the Harbour Branch Oceanographic Institute, a private, non-profit group based in Fort Pierce, Fla.

In respect of the expense of submersibles: 'It will do water-quality measurements, biological studies, plankton counts and all the basic research missions,' said Dan White, the project manager at Harbour Branch. 'It could do fish counts, or sand movements. In South Florida we have hundreds of kilometres of reefs. You might want to run down them once or twice a year. There are an infinite number of missions you could perform.'

Dr Cindy Van Dover, a biological oceanographer at Woods Hole who is a former pilot of the Alvin submersible, echoed Dr Bellingham, saying the great cost of manned missions for deep sea exploration limited the ability of scientists to do important work on the planet's last frontier.

'Submersibles are not enough,' she said. 'We have a small number, and they're expensive. Getting time on them is more a prose game than science game, using the right words to sell an idea.'

Even undersea robots for basic science are in a relatively primitive stage of evolution. Dr Van Dover added: 'There are more of them and they can stay down much longer. They can study how things change over time. That's a very powerful ability, I think they'll go far.'

These interviews and comments by some of the leading exponents of deep-sea exploration provide an insight into current and future thinking and trends. Man alone cannot reach such depths, and man in machines is expensive, but an autonomous machine can provide us with vital information.

The Advanced Unmanned Search System (AUSS) is the latest autonomous underwater vehicle to be developed by the Naval Command Control and Ocean Surveillance Centre RDT & E Division of the United States Navy in San Diego. The AUSS is designed to locate, identify and inspect objects on the seabed at depths of 610–6,100 m (2,000–20,000 ft), and embraces the latest technology in navigation, search capability and image systems.

A small, untethered vehicle, it provides sonar and optical images of the ocean bottom to operators on a ship thousands of metres above. The operators analyse the images, make operational decisions, and supervise the vehicle's control system. An acoustic link transmits compressed search data from the vehicle to the surface and allows high-level commands to be sent to the vehicle. The operators can then acoustically command the vehicle where to go and what to do, but not how to do it. The vehicle performs each task until it is completed or until the operators interrupt with a new command.

The vehicle's computers use a Doppler sonar and gyrocompass to perform onboard navigation, so that in effect, the vehicle always knows where it is in Doppler coordinates. The vehicle can be commanded to go to a specific location and hover there, or to execute large search patterns, without assistance. It has a side-looking sonar (SLS) for the rapid search of large areas and a scanning, forward-looking sonar (FLS) for closing in on sonar targets. A charge coupled device (CCD), which involves an electronic stills camera, is used to identify false targets and to perform detailed inspections of targets of interest. It is fitted with a 35mm photographic camera for recording and documentation purposes.

Data from the electronic search sensors is formatted into discrete images which are compressed and acoustically transmit-

Figure 15: *The Advanced Unmanned Search System (AUSS).* (US Navy)

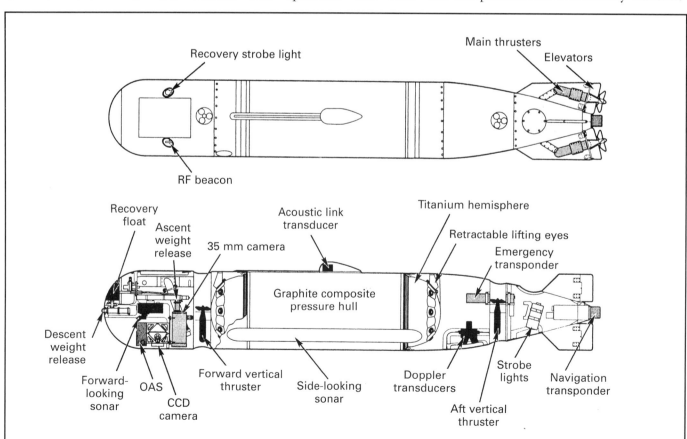

ted to the surface. Vehicle navigation data within the images permits an operator to obtain the Doppler coordinates of objects by placing a cursor over the image and marking it by a simple keystroke.

The two highest-level commands are the SLS search command and the optical photomosaic. In both, the operator defines a rectangular area of the bottom to be covered and the vehicle proceeds autonomously in a square wave pattern while continuously transmitting images. The photomosaic command can be used for optical search, or as a technique for optical inspection and documentation of an area.

SLS is the primary sensor for search. When a likely contact is seen on the SLS display, search may be suspended and the object immediately investigated, or alternatively the target may be marked for later investigation. If the target is not the one which was sought, a single command will cause the search to be resumed from where it was suspended. If the target is the object sought, various techniques are available for performing detailed optical inspection.

The AUSS system consists of the vehicle, a control van, a maintenance van, a launch and recovery ramp, and a shallow tow fish for acoustic communications. The system easily fits on an offshore supply boat, which means that it does not require a specially fitted or adapted vessel, and so keeps operational costs to a minimum.

The centre section of the AUSS vehicle is a cylindrical graphite epoxy pressure hull with titanium hemispherical endbells. The hull provides the central structure of the vehicle and all the buoyancy needed. External pressure housings are titanium. The freely flooded forward and aft end fairings and structure are of a nearly buoyant composite. Two main thrusters provide forward and aft propulsion and steering. Two vertical thrusters, one forward and one aft, provide vertical propulsion and affect pitch trim at low speeds. Elevators provide vertical control at high speeds. The silver zinc battery endurance is 10 hours at the maximum velocity of 5 knots.

The vehicle deployment system uses a launch ramp with one end floating and the other gimballed to the deck. The vehicle is rolled from the maintenance van onto the ramp which is then extended overboard, and the bottom end is lowered to float on the ocean's surface. The vehicle is released to slide down the ramp and is pulled to the bottom of the ocean on a weighted line. At the end of the operation, the vehicle drops ascent weights, floats to the surface, and is recovered up the ramp. In 3,048 m (10,000 ft) of water the ascent and descent each take about 30 minutes.

A major advantage of AUSS is its capability to identify sonar contacts quickly when on an SLS search run, by continuously transmitting sonar images to the surface via the acoustic link. The AUSS operators notice a contact in an SLS image, whereupon they command the vehicle to interrupt the search and come to a stop. The target is marked to determine the approximate Doppler coordinates of the contact from the SLS image. They then command the vehicle to go to a distance of 23 m (75 ft) from the contact, and carry out an FLS scan. They then mark the target to obtain revised Doppler coordinates from the FLS image before commanding the vehicle to go to the new coordinates. At the new coordinates they will request a CCD image, which they will evaluate. They will then command the vehicle to continue with the search. The vehicle autonomously returns to the interrupted search track and resumes sending SLS images.

The great flexibility of AUSS is most apparent in performing inspections. Once a CCD image revealing an important object is received, the controllers have a number of options available to them in order that a more detailed inspection can be undertaken. The system can transmit one or more of the previous CCD images at higher resolution. They can identify, mark a portion of an image and move over that location, hover at a higher or lower altitude, and take another CCD image. They also have the ability to turn the 35mm camera on or off, take a series of pictures while moving in any direction, do an optical photomosaic area coverage, or back away and take another FLS scan at higher resolution or at longer range. This makes the AUSS vehicle a very flexible and efficient underwater tool.

AUSS has accomplished almost all of the goals that were planned for the programme, and some of the most exciting accomplishments have resulted from the adaptability of the system during a search and the post-search image processing. The system's accomplishments include 89 dives to a depth of 762 m (2,500 ft) with a prototype system, and 45 dives at depths of 762–3,657 m (2,500–12,000 ft) with the final system. The scope of work of which the vehicle is capable includes: a very detailed SLS search facility; immediate contact evaluations; operator-directed inspections; optical photomosaics using film and/or CCD; successful searches and inspections with and without acoustic tracking transponder fields; and sustained area search rates, including contact evaluations.

The Naval Command, Control and Ocean Surveillance Centre (NCCOSC) has been a pioneer in the area of underwater vehicles and work systems since the mid-1960s. The AUSS system is considered to be amongst the most advanced search systems in the world today. The system design depth is 6,100 m (20,000 ft), with successful operations undertaken to a depth of 3,657 m (12,000 ft) off the southern California coast in June 1992. By the time this book is published, further programmes will have taken it to its maximum operating depth.

Technological areas that have been advanced by the AUSS programme include the supervisory control of remote underwater vehicles, high data transmission rate of underwater acoustic communications, autonomous control of remote underwater vehicles, the use of non-metallic materials for pressure hulls, and the operational applications of unmanned underwater vehicles to the problems of undertaking searches in the deep oceans. The development of the AUSS system is directly applicable to other underwater research and investigations, which means that scientific areas such as oceanography, biology, geology, ocean exploitation, environmental monitoring and sub-bottom profiling could be aided by this technology, to name but a few.

The final word on deep ocean robotics rests with the US Navy but reflects the thinking of all engaged in deep underwater research and work. Unmanned, untethered underwater vehicles are the next generation of deep ocean sensor platforms – the 'eyes and ears' for the inquisitive in all the depths and expanses of the planet's seas and oceans.

Chapter 11

Seabed Vehicles

AS THE DEVELOPMENT of the North Sea oil and gas production facilities spread over a wider area, more pipelines were required to carry the oil or gas to the shore, and from satellite platforms to central production facilities. Some fields were small and did not warrant the major investment of installing a platform, so they have been developed by the use of sub-sea wellheads. These are not visible from the surface, but are served by pipelines and electrical and hydraulic power cables from a central platform. All of these cables and pipelines are vital to production and safety.

In the early days of North Sea exploration, the pipelines carrying gas from the platforms in the southern sector to the terminals on land were laid on the seabed and not buried. A major problem here that had not been foreseen was that there are very strong currents in this area of the North Sea, which is shallower and narrower than the northern sector. This caused the pipelines physically to move across the seabed, which meant that the carrier of gas was liable to be severely damaged, with potentially serious consequences.

The first and most active response to this problem was to cover the pipelines with specially designed mattresses which moulded themselves over the pipeline and into the seabed. To aid the retention of the sand around the pipeline, scour mats made of nets with plastic fronds protruding from them were developed. These nets were supposed to collect and retain the moving sand in order to create a sand bar. Some were successful, but others were washed away by the current. The one thing they were all good at was trapping the divers who laid them and other divers in the fronds – it was hard work to get free. Apart from the scour problems, the pipelines were susceptible to damage from ships' anchors and fishing boat trawls, the latter being a major problem both then and now, as fishing boats seek the fish that congregate around the structures and pipelines.

The obvious answer was to remove the object that could be damaged and that meant that the pipelines needed to the buried. Early methods were experimental and simply a matter of trial and error. The trial could be expensive, but so could damage to a pipeline. The basic types of unit used involved an uncontrolled dredge type that made a trench for the pipeline to be laid in, allowing a natural backfill. This required a unit to plough, air lift or water jet the seabed away. Others were dragged along the pipeline or cable and jetted the seabed away, allowing the pipeline to settle in the trench. These were not the best methods as there was little control over the operation. In the northern sector the water depth was such that it was at first considered safe for pipelines not to be buried, but some of the problems that had been encountered in the southern sector with ships' anchors and trawlers were found in the north and so many of the pipelines and electrical cables were buried there as well.

One of the first answers to the question of how to bury pipelines came in the form of 'jet barges'. These were large floating barges which followed behind the pipe-laying barge. They towed a sled device that blasted a trench into the seabed by means of multiple high-pressure water jets. The jets were closely spaced and arranged in two vertical rows which, incorporated into a device called a 'claw', straddled the pipeline. The jet nozzles in each row were staggered so that they pointed in different directions. Also straddling the pipeline and mounted behind each row of jets were two air lift pipes that sucked the mud or sand out of the trench after it had been blasted loose by the jets.

The jetting equipment was set on two pontoons, which made the bases for the sled, and while this ran along the seabed, the 'claw' could be adjusted for the depth of the trench that was required. The jets cut and broke up the seabed, which was then sucked into the dredge to be thrown out to the side, clear of the pipeline and trench.

This equipment could operate down to a depth of about 61 m (200 ft), but beyond that difficulties were encountered because the length of hoses and cables that were required became a handling problem and were subject to failure. The system also required large pumps to provide suitable pressure for jetting and suction and that was less effective in deeper water. It was also necessary to rely on the crew of the vessel to control the direction of the sled, which had no system of steering. The setting of the sled and the progress and success of the burial operation required the services of divers, who operated from the barge. Their reports were verbal because at that time underwater televisions were large and cumbersome, being in their infancy and not in general use.

It was evident that a more effective and controllable method of burial was required, and so the development of seabed tractors began. The basic concept was for a vehicle that could follow a pipeline or cable, using underwater television cameras as a method of control. It would be able to cut a trench, lay the pipe or cable and then bury it. The first such design was the 'Sea Bug', developed by the British company UDI. That first vehicle may well have taken a lesson from the land, for it had four large tractor tyres on

wheels which were part of a chassis on to which the unit's equipment was fitted. It could be steered remotely, from the surface, and was designed to operate to a depth of 183 m (600 ft). An umbilical from a surface support vessel supplied power, TV signals to and from the cameras, and underwater lights. All operations involved in lifting the cable, cutting the trench and burying it were controlled by a surface operator, who had a bank of TV monitors and a joystick control system that enabled him to steer the 'Bug', operate the articulated arm and pan and tilt the television cameras.

In many ways the 'Sea Bug' was ahead of its time, and it did suffer many teething problems. That said, its equipment fit was impressive. It had a crane with a 5 m (16 ft) reach. A three-dimensional arm and manipulator enabled it to carry out inspection of both sides of a pipeline in one run, using either colour or black and white television camera systems, with a relay to the surface for video recording. At that time still photographs were generally used for recording activities, especially for reports, and the 'Bug' carried an 800-shot still camera. Apart from using television cameras for control purposes, the 'Bug' was also fitted with sonars and a gyro compass.

The concept of the 'Sea Bug' did not die, and UDI used the knowledge and experience gained to progress the design into a new remote-controlled trenching and cable burial system. This differed from the 'Bug' in that it utilized tracks instead of wheels. The wheels had proved to be an operational problem, affecting the steering. Experiments showed that tracks eliminated most of the problems and allowed the vehicle to travel at speed, while enabling the operator to control the direction by using an improved drive control system.

The vehicle was fitted with a 3 ton plough that was said to be able to cut a precise, clean trench to depths of between 0.6 m and 1 m (2–3 ft). The vehicle had a specially developed self-steering mechanism which enabled the plough to follow the pipeline even if the vehicle had to manoeuvre around seabed obstructions.

The soil drawn from the trench was piled to one side of it and drawn into the trench on a second run, when the vehicle's plough was replaced with a blade. All of this was said to be possible to an operational depth of 300 m (985 ft).

Launching the vehicle was accomplished with the help of an 'A' frame sited at the stern of a vessel equipped with a basic dynamic positioned (DP) system. The vehicle's umbilical, which supplied the power and enabled the sending and receiving of television transmissions, was constructed in such a way that it could be used as the lift cable. The vehicle's crane was hydraulic but had the addition of a manipulator with full rotational and gripping actions. The vehicle was fitted with six television cameras to provide a complete surveillance package.

While UDI and the offshore oil and gas industry were struggling with new designs for burial vehicles and equipment, the telecommunications industry was encountering similar problems. With a worldwide demand for more and better communications, there evolved a need for more sub-sea telecommunications cables to be laid. This has resulted in the telecommunications companies laying and burying hundreds of kilometres of fibre-optic cables in water depths up to 1,000 m (3,281 ft).

Initially, the cables only needed to be buried in more shallow waters, where the delicate fibre-optic cables were susceptible to damage from fishermen's trawls or ships' anchors. Today, however, fishermen have moved their operations into much deeper water, often with bottom trawls, and therefore the most effective protection is to bury the cables.

If the answer is for the owners of pipelines and cables to bury them then they have to address the problems caused by currents which can be very strong, resulting in movement of the seabed. This means that what is buried one week can be exposed a week later. Careful research into seabed conditions prior to pipeline or cable laying can offer a formula for initial burial and remedial action if it should become exposed at a later date. Where it is known that pipelines or cables will not

remain buried, other options are available, including specially designed and constructed mattresses or concrete covers which can be laid along the pipeline. This is expensive, but it reduces the risk of damage and the resulting loss of communications or pollution, depending upon what is damaged.

Most pipeline and cable burial operations are conducted during the laying process or immediately after. The United Kingdom has emerged as a world leader in the development of burial systems. Many problems had to be overcome at the design stage, beginning with the forma-

The 'Sea Dog' is a large, tracked underwater cable-burying machine. It is able to pick up the cable, jet a trench and lay it in. (Slingsby Engineering)

tion of the seabed in which the burial has to take place and the design of a system that can undertake the job. There is the need to place electronics, electrically powered motors and hydraulic systems in a harsh underwater environment, and in water depths of up to 1,000 m (3,281 ft). On land, or even on the deck of a support vessel, an item of equipment that becomes damaged and unserviceable can be repaired. If the unit is underwater, at depth, it has to be recovered in order that repairs can be made. That is time-consuming and costly. The most critical time for damage to equipment is during launch and recovery operations.

Another early design for a basic seabed burial system for pipelines was the sand lift trencher. It was designed to bury pipelines after they had been laid, but it had limitations in that it could only work in suitable seabed material. The principal operation of the system was that the seabed under and to the side of the pipeline was fluidized by water jets. The material was then drawn into an airlift and ejected away. For normal burial operations the depth would be up to 1 m (3 ft), but with extensions a depth of 1.5 m (5 ft) could be obtained. Pressurized water for the jetting aspect of the operation was provided by four submersible, electrically driven pumps mounted on the unit, with the electrical power generated on the surface support vessel and supplied through an umbilical. The air supply, provided from compressors on the surface support vessel, also came through an umbilical to the unit.

The unit was placed over the pipeline, and this aspect of the operation may well have required the services of a diver to ensure that it was in position. The jetting and suction pumps were activated, removing the seabed from below and to the sides of the pipeline. The support vessel moved ahead, pulling the unit along the pipeline and causing it to lay down in the newly formed trench. The seabed was left to refill the trench, to the original level, by natural movement.

One experienced cable-laying company is BT Marine, the wholly owned subsidiary of British Telecommunications Plc.

They are involved in every aspect of submarine cable-laying systems. The experience they have gained over the years has now extended beyond just laying telecommunication cables, and has evolved techniques for the combined operation of laying and burial. The major handling systems include two Submersible Plough Systems, a Modular Plough System and a Submersible Trencher. Deployment of the cable and burial system is undertaken by 'A' frame and a special carousel and gantry system. BT's Submersible Plough is designed to cut into sand and clay so that the soil is not moved to the side after being excavated and then backfilled. This means that the clay and sand retain their strength, leaving a level soil surface with only two knife cuts to show that the system has passed by. The pilot, in a control cabin on the surface support vessel, uses television cameras fitted to the plough to observe the route and has a limited ability to steer the unit around seabed obstructions whilst it is under tow.

The Modular Plough System is a basic unit of plough, control cabin, umbilical and handling equipment which can be placed upon a surface support vessel and is able to lay and bury cables or umbilicals up to 200 mm (8 in) in diameter down to a depth of 1.4 m (4.6 ft) below the seabed surface. The Trenching Plough has two plough shares and two front and rear pipe support cradles fitted to the unit's chassis. The shares rotate and allow the cable roller cradles to open, then lower and engage the cable. The unit is then lifted into the ploughing position and the laying and burying operation can begin.

Soil Machine Dynamics (SMD) is a British company which is a world leader in underwater plough and tractor development. Their expertise is sought worldwide by customers such as the Transpacific Communications Corporation of the USA, a subsidiary of AT & T, who ordered a plough, which was designated *Sea Plow VI*. It was rated for operations in water depths of up to 1,000 m (3,281 ft), and to bury cables up to 100 mm (4 in) in diameter and repeaters and junction boxes up to 400 mm (16 in) in diameter, all to a depth of 1.2 m (4 ft) below the seabed. A powerful unit, it is able to cut through weak clays or sand to medium rock. The unit design requirement was for a trouble-free system that could be deployed to bury cable during the laying operation or be able to undertake a burial operation on cables that had already been laid. Because of the depth of water in which cable-burying operations were required, a key design feature was that it should be diverless.

In the burial operation, the plough share and cutting disc work in conjunction to remove a wedge of material sideways and upwards, allowing the cable to be laid. After the share has passed, the material is replaced over the cable. In normal combined lay and bury operations the plough is launched and recovered with the cable installed and running freely so that no strain is applied to the cable. This is essential when laying cables in deep water because the greater strain created could cause damage to the more delicate fibre-optic cables. For operations that require pre-laid cables to be buried, the plough is fitted with navigation aids which allow the unit to be placed extremely accurately on the seabed. For the final positioning, two horizontal thrusters and underwater television cameras allow the pilot to manoeuvre the unit. A crane fitted to the plough can then lift the cable and load it into the unit.

The *Sea Plow* is controlled remotely, from a control cabin on the surface support ship, through an armoured umbilical. The control room has two operators, each of whom has an independent graphics display panel. These are interlinked to provide simultaneous monitoring of the plough's condition and work progress. TV cameras relay pictures to the console of the principal working parts and condition of the cable. An obstacle avoidance sonar relays vital information about the seabed conditions, which enables the plough to be steered in order to avoid obstructions and determine suitable routes. As is standard in today's underwater operations, the entire operation is recorded on video and a data logging system provides a detailed record of the operation.

The undersea cable construction company AT & T Submarine Systems, based in Morristown, New Jersey, USA, sought to upgrade its operations by developing a compact, unmanned and tracked seabed

The control panel of an SMD plough or tractor system. From this unit the operations taking place on the seabed are monitored and recorded. Two operators have duplicate information systems to ensure effective control. The fan shapes on the screens are the sonar scans. (SMD)

work vehicle. British underwater technology was proved again as SMD turned its experience with ploughs to a tracked vehicle. As a result, AT & T was provided with the Sea Bed Tractor system which was suitable for the company's operations in the USA and other regions. Apart from the development of the tractor, SMD had to develop the control umbilical, a launch and recovery system (LARS), a surface unit and control module. The design was for a powerful vehicle that could bury cables equally well in water depths of 1,400 m (4,593 ft), shallow waters, beach zones and tidal waters.

Traction of the vehicle is by two caterpillar tracks, which enables it to work in a wide variety of water and seabed conditions. It has two trenching tools, a jetting sled and rock wheel cutter. The jetting device is designed to cut a trench to a depth of 1 m (3 ft) in sand or clay. For greater flexibility the rock wheel cutter will cut a trench 1 m deep in compacted sand and clays and also medium rock. Jetting is a very inefficient method of moving soil, especially if it is compacted, but it has the advantage that its cutting action will not damage the cable. It was with this

in mind that SMD designed the SBT to be equipped with a very simple unguarded tool that can be deployed down onto the cable for the burial process; it has the advantage that it can easily be lifted off if the tractor breaks down and needs to be recovered.

When comparing the advantages and disadvantages of the tractor or the plough, the overall burial operation, including seabed conditions, will have to be evaluated in order to determine the most suitable system to use. A major advantage for the tractor is its ability to operate on beaches and in surf conditions and so bury cables from the shore to water depths of 1,400 m (4,593 ft). It can cope with soft materials or rock that needs to be cut. All systems and operational procedures are developed on the basis that divers will not be required.

A key element of deep water burial is that when the tractor is at depth in the ocean, the operator is on the support vessel and therefore requires an extensive range of transducers to measure heading, altitude, inclination, and data on the progress of the burial. The information is transmitted to the operator through a fibre-optic umbilical cable. Part of the overall control and system status are five television cameras, an obstacle avoidance sonar, a hydrophone and a magnetic cable tracker.

As with all operations at sea involving working with sophisticated equipment, the weather plays a very important part. A cable lay operation is most effective if the weather conditions allow the vessel to continue working, and the most critical time will be during the launch and recovery of the tractor. SMD have developed the Launch and Recovery System (LARS) which can transport the tractor from the deck of the vessel to a position over the stern using a hydraulically operated 'A' frame. Integrated into the 'A' frame is a docking head that stabilizes the tractor during its surface movement. As the tractor descends to the depths the umbilical is paid out, and buoyancy is attached to offset the weight and the cable catenary. Because the system is modular it can be installed on a wide range of suitable vessels, of which dynamic positioned vessels (DP) are the most effective.

While SMD developed the Sea Bed Tractor, the US company Perry Tritech

worked on the Flexjet Trencher, which combines the two proven concepts of a bottom crawler and a remote operated vehicle (ROV). The hub of the system is the field-proven *Triton* ROV, which incorporates the systems controls and hydraulic power unit and is able to transfer those controls to the crawler unit. The unit is deployed into the water using a crane, as

The Perry Tritech Flexjet I trencher is a tracked unit controlled from the surface. It is able to bury small cable by jetting out a trench. (Perry Tritech)

The cable ship Mercury *is one of Cable and Wireless's six repair ships stationed at strategic locations around the world. The ships are equipped to carry and lay cables in all seas and oceans. Modern cables are fibre-optic and require careful handling to avoid damage. If repairs are needed, the* Cirrus *ROV is used to locate the damage and assist in the recovery of the cable to the ship where a repair splice can be made. (Cable & Wireless Marine)*

The protected cable, with a larger diameter than normal, is fed along a conveyor system along the deck of the vessel. The device at the top aids its movement. (Northern Ocean Services)

and be positioned over the cable or pipeline. It is then lowered on to the seabed and made negatively buoyant, placing all of its weight onto the crawler tracks. The trench is cut by a high-pressure jetting system that restricts the use of the vehicle to soft materials as there is no provision for cutting rock. An advantage with this vehicle is that it can work on an exposed section of cable or pipeline, and then be flown to the next exposed section without having to be recovered. By using a DP vessel the ROV's transponder can be used as a position reference and the vehicle followed as it moves along the pipeline. A unique feature of the unit is that the crawler and jetting system can be separated from the ROV, allowing the *Triton* to be operated as a stand-alone, heavy work ROV system.

Cable and Wireless (Marine) lay telecommunication cables in every sea and ocean in the world and have to overcome the myriad of problems facing those operations. Laying a cable and burying it is one aspect of the work, but cables do develop problems and have to be repaired.

would be the case with a conventional ROV. In the water the unit is deballasted, allowing it to sink to the seabed, with the umbilical being paid out as it descends. The vehicle can hover above the seabed

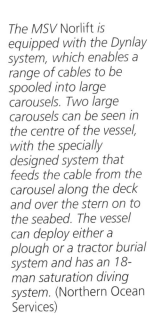

The MSV Norlift *is equipped with the Dynlay system, which enables a range of cables to be spooled into large carousels. Two large carousels can be seen in the centre of the vessel, with the specially designed system that feeds the cable from the carousel along the deck and over the stern on to the seabed. The vessel can deploy either a plough or a tractor burial system and has an 18-man saturation diving system. (Northern Ocean Services)*

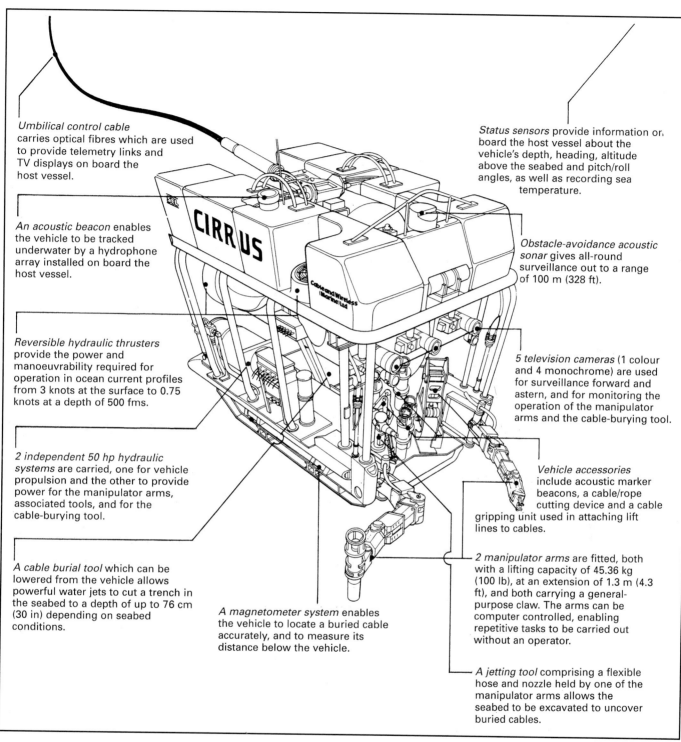

Umbilical control cable carries optical fibres which are used to provide telemetry links and TV displays on board the host vessel.

Status sensors provide information on board the host vessel about the vehicle's depth, heading, altitude above the seabed and pitch/roll angles, as well as recording sea temperature.

An acoustic beacon enables the vehicle to be tracked underwater by a hydrophone array installed on board the host vessel.

Obstacle-avoidance acoustic sonar gives all-round surveillance out to a range of 100 m (328 ft).

Reversible hydraulic thrusters provide the power and manoeuvrability required for operation in ocean current profiles from 3 knots at the surface to 0.75 knots at a depth of 500 fms.

5 television cameras (1 colour and 4 monochrome) are used for surveillance forward and astern, and for monitoring the operation of the manipulator arms and the cable-burying tool.

2 independent 50 hp hydraulic systems are carried, one for vehicle propulsion and the other to provide power for the manipulator arms, associated tools, and for the cable-burying tool.

Vehicle accessories include acoustic marker beacons, a cable/rope cutting device and a cable gripping unit used in attaching lift lines to cables.

A cable burial tool which can be lowered from the vehicle allows powerful water jets to cut a trench in the seabed to a depth of up to 76 cm (30 in) depending on seabed conditions.

2 manipulator arms are fitted, both with a lifting capacity of 45.36 kg (100 lb), at an extension of 1.3 m (4.3 ft), and both carrying a general-purpose claw. The arms can be computer controlled, enabling repetitive tasks to be carried out without an operator.

A magnetometer system enables the vehicle to locate a buried cable accurately, and to measure its distance below the vehicle.

A jetting tool comprising a flexible hose and nozzle held by one of the manipulator arms allows the seabed to be excavated to uncover buried cables.

In a vast expanse of sea, the cable, and in particular the damaged section, has to be located, and while a ship can use a Global Positioning System for general navigation, a cable which is buried under the seabed in 1,400 m (4,593 ft) of water requires a special search tool. Cable and Wireless use the *Cirrus* ROV, which was designed and equipped for cable location. The vehicle has the normal equipment found on modern ROVs, but with additional tools to meet the task. A magnetometer system enables the vehicle to locate a buried cable accurately, and to measure its distance below the vehicle. When the buried cable is located, the exact fault point has to be

Figure 16: *The systems and functions of the Cable and Wireless* Cirrus *ROV, which was developed to carry out work on the cables that are laid on and under the seabed.*

found and identified and that involves more electronic equipment. When this has been achieved a jetting tool, comprising a flexible hose and nozzle held by one of the vehicle's manipulators, allows the seabed to be excavated to uncover the buried cable. The vehicle is also fitted with a cable burial tool that can be lowered from the vehicle, allowing powerful water jets to cut a trench in the seabed to a depth of up to .8 m (1 ft 6 in) depending on the seabed conditions.

There have without doubt been both successes and failures using the burial equipment described, but that is only to be expected given the environment in which they have to work. Each new job presents a challenge which has to be met and overcome.

Chapter 12

Deep Ocean Research

Woods Hole

The Woods Hole Oceanographic Institution (WHOI) is the largest independent oceanographic laboratory in the world. Its shore-based facilities are located in the village of Woods Hole and on the 200 acre Quissett Campus overlooking Vineyard Sound. The staff, who number about a thousand, include scientists, engineers, technicians, graduate students, postdoctoral scholars, and visiting fellows from around the world.

It wasn't until the late 19th century that a name was given to the science of the sea. The great European research expeditions of the 1800s measured the depths of the deep oceans, and the salinity and temperature of different water masses. These expeditions also recorded the surprising diversity of marine life and the characteristics of bottom rocks and sediment.

In 1927 a National Academy of Sciences committee concluded that it was time to 'consider the share of the United States of America in a worldwide programme of oceanographic research'. The Academy recommended establishing a permanent independent research laboratory on the east coast to 'prosecute oceanography in all its branches'. Thus, the Woods Hole Oceanographic Institution was founded in 1930 with a $3 million grant from the Rockefeller Foundation to support about a dozen scientists, to build a laboratory, and to commission a research vessel, the 43 m (142 ft) ketch *Atlantis*.

WHOI's ships carry out investigations throughout the world's oceans to conduct highly diverse research ranging from tracking currents and pollutants in coastal waters to examining ancient climates by measuring the gases trapped in tiny air bubbles frozen in polar ice.

The Institution operates many specialized laboratories with state-of-the-art equipment. Examples include an accelerator mass spectrometer used by the international oceanographic community for radiocarbon dating, and a 17 m (56 ft) long flume, unique in its ability to simulate precisely the flow of water at the sea floor. Success is directly dependent on the tools they use to observe, take measurements, and gather samples in an unpredictable and hostile environment. WHOI's engineers, like its scientists, are world-renowned for their excellence and innovation and oceanographers throughout the world use instruments developed at WHOI.

The deep diving research submarine *Alvin*, with its crew of three, is a result of WHOI's commitment to deep submergence engineering. The Institution's engineers have also been at the forefront of unmanned Remotely Operated Vehicle (ROV) technology. The *Jason/Medea* ROV system developed by WHOI's Centre for Marine Exploration uses fibre-optic cable to send video images to banks of television monitors aboard ship. The underwater images can be transmitted live anywhere in the world via satellite.

Education is an important part of the Institution's development policy and in 1968 WHOI and the Massachusetts Institute of Technology (MIT) established the Joint Programme in Oceanography/Applied Ocean Science and Engineering. Every year, about 130 graduate students in the Joint Programme work toward Masters or doctoral degrees, either at Woods Hole or at MIT in Cambridge, Massachusetts.

WHOI offer one-year fellowships to postdoctoral scholars, and summer fellowships to recent college graduates and undergraduates who have completed at least their junior years. In addition, guest students at both graduate and undergraduate levels spend varying amounts of time at the Institution working with individual scientists. The Institute also hosts workshops for college science teachers, and participates in many other educational projects involving students from the primary grades through high school.

Those with a special interest in the work and projects of Woods Hole can become members of the Young Associates of WHOI and receive regular information and copies of the magazine *Ocean Explorer*. In addition, Associates and Affiliates of WHOI receive copies of *Woods Hole Currents* magazine, which keeps them up to date on the Institute's research programmes, as well as other items of a more general interest.

In 1991, youngsters in the USA were treated to some unusual lessons. Some 7,623 students crowded into the WHOI Redfield Building and more than half a million others attended 20 specially equipped centres in the USA and Canada to participate in live broadcasts from the Galapagos Islands in the Pacific Ocean. This was the third project carried out by the Jason Foundation for Education, which is a non-profit-making body made up of industrial, educational and research organizations. The Foundation was formed in 1989 by the WHOI marine geologist Bob Ballard, with the aim of bringing the adventure and drama of underwater research directly to young students in a way that would enable them to take an active part. On this occasion they were able to participate in hour-long broadcasts hosted by Bob Ballard. This was a busy time for WHOI as there were five broadcasts a day six days a week.

The first Jason project was broadcast in 1989 from the Mediterranean, where an exploration of an ancient shipwreck and a study of an underwater volcanic site were taking place. The following year the *Jason* ROV explored two shipwrecks from the 1812 war in Lake Ontario. The 1991 project included broadcasts from both land and underwater. During the project students were able to speak direct to scientists, including biologist Gerard Wellington, who was wearing a wet suit and a clear plastic bubble helmet over his head. As another diver used a video camera to film him, he waved from his research location 10 m (30 ft) underwater off North Seymore Islands in the Galapagos. He then, through the link-up, answered questions posed by the students, who were able to watch him on large video screens and so be involved in the activity of underwater research as it happened.

The ocean, which covers some 70 per cent of our planet's surface, is the single largest environment on Earth, but the marine world encompasses much more than just the oceans and sea, because it also embraces rivers, estuaries, marshes and coasts; the chasms, mountains and trenches at the sea floor, among the deepest and tallest structures on earth; the midwater regions where most marine life exists; and the sunlit waters where plants are able to photosynthesize, and where critical gases pass to and from the atmosphere in a complex process that determines the climate and, ultimately, the weather which affects the entire world.

At WHOI's Coastal Research Centre, investigators from all departments focus on the processes underway in the water nearest their shores, the area that is most affected by the activities of human beings. Oceanographers specialize in various scientific disciplines, including biology, chemistry, geology, physics and meteorology. In keeping with oceanography's intrinsically multidisciplinary nature, many marine scientists combine their fields of expertise into, for instance, biogeochemistry or geophysics. Each investigator decides what research problem to pursue. It is also the scientists' responsibility to acquire funding to support their research.

The Ocean Drilling Program

The Ocean Drilling Program (ODP) sponsors an international partnership of scientists and governments to explore the Earth's last frontier, its structure and its history, beneath the seabed. This allows scientists to sail the world's oceans in consecutive cruises on board the drill ship *JOIDES Resolution*. During these cruises, each approximately eight weeks long, scientists drill holes deep into the sea floor to penetrate millions of years of Earth's geologic history.

The United States National Science Foundation funds the ODP in conjunction with significant contributions from member countries. The participating members of the Joint Oceanographic Institutions for Deep Earth Sampling (JOIDES) are from a worldwide network of universities, oceanographic institutions and government agencies.

A programme of this magnitude and investment requires first-class management and therefore Texas A & M University, Texas, USA, serves as the science operator for the programme as well as operating and staffing the drill ship. Texas A & M is also responsible for the retrieval of core samples from sites around the world.

On board the ship, Texas A & M maintains the laboratories and provides logistical and technical support for the scientific teams. Onshore, Texas A & M manages scientific meetings before and after cruises, curates the cores from the Pacific and Indian Oceans, distributes samples and edits and publishes the scientific results.

The Lamont-Doherty Geological Observatory of Columbia University in Palisades, New York, manages the wireline logging and the JOIDES/ODP site survey data bank and stores cores retrieved from the Atlantic Ocean. West Coast Repository at Scripps Institution of Oceanography in La Jolla, California, stores all cores retrieved from the Pacific and Indian Oceans by the previous Deep Sea Drilling Project and the current Ocean Drilling Programs.

Investigating the Earth's origin and evolution through the technology of scientific ocean drilling would not be possible without a uniquely outfitted drill ship. The ship, officially registered as *Sedco/BP471*, is known to the scientific community by its informal name, *JOIDES Resolution*. It is 143 m (470 ft) long and 21 m (70 ft) wide. The drilling tower rises more than 62 m (200 ft) above the waterline. To remain on location the ship has a com-

The JOIDES Resolution, *the drill ship for the Ocean Drilling Programme. The uniquely outfitted drill ship makes it possible to investigate the Earth's origin and evolution through scientific ocean drilling. The ship can drill in water depths up to 8 km (5 miles) and can deploy almost 9.6 km (6 miles) of drill string. It contains the world's most advanced research equipment, together with electronics, photographic, computer and library facilities for the 115 scientists and crew. (Texas A & M University)*

The core is 9.5 m (31 ft) in length when it is recovered from the drill string. It is taken to the core receiving station where the team record each section's length and the depth from which it was retrieved from beneath the seabed. The core is then cut into manageable lengths of 1.5 m (5 ft) and each section is then split in half. (Texas A & M University)

After the core has been split in half, one half is worked upon on board the ship and the other half is recorded and put into storage. It is then made available to a wide variety of organizations through Texas A & M University, to support research programmes undertaken without access to the ship. (Texas A & M University)

puter-controlled dynamic positioning system which allows drilling in water depths of up to 8,200 m (27,000 ft).

The ship's 12 laboratories contain the world's most advanced research equipment, so scientists on board have at their disposal a complete range of instruments. Representing a variety of disciplines in earth sciences, they analyse samples of rock, examine smears of sediment under an array of microscopes, X-ray cores with sophisticated machines, probe thick rounds of samples with thermometers, and compress, freeze or slice the sub-sea floor material. Although the analyses done on board the ship provide information critical to the programme's mission, the recovered rocks and sediment also become invaluable resources for scientists around the world. The scientists also study palaeontology, petrology, geochemistry, geophysics, paleomagnetics and physical properties, and a cryogenic magnetometer records the history of reversals in the Earth's magnetic field.

The Ocean Drilling Program began its eighth year of operation in 1992, its predecessor, the Deep Sea Drilling Project, having operated from 1968 to 1983. This means that more than 20 years of drilling have enabled scientists to greatly advance what we know about the fundamental processes and structure of planet Earth.

Scientists now know more about the origin and evolution of ocean crust, the tectonic evolution of continental margins and the processes of plate collision. They have been able to study ancient environmental conditions including long-term changes in Earth's atmosphere, oceans, polar regions and biosphere.

Since January 1985, the *JOIDES Resolution* has drilled extensively in the Atlantic, Pacific and Indian Oceans, recovering more than 77,515 m (254,326 ft) of core. It has explored the Mediterranean, Norwegian, Labrador, Weddell, Sulu, Celebes, Philippine and Japan Seas. It has also successfully tested its high-latitude capabilities north of the Arctic and south of the Antarctic Circles. Scientists from more than 30 nations have addressed scientific objectives relating to the history of ancient oceanic environments, and the origin and evolution of ocean crust, continental margins and sediment layers.

As a result of scientific demands the ODP through Texas A & M University has identified the need to develop new technology in order that the *JOIDES Resolution*

can be used to drill in highly fractured for-mations, which historically have had poor hole stability and low rates of core recov-ery. The task will be to recover all types of sediments, including alternating hard and soft lithologies and unconsolidated sands, as well as to withstand the extremely high temperatures in areas where material from deep within the earth spews onto the seabed. Within the holes that are drilled scientists can place earthquake monitoring devices and other instruments for long-term data monitoring.

A major aim for the future will be to drill deeper into the crust than ever before. This will allow today's scientists as well as those of future generations to con-tinue to analyse the cores that ODP retrieves from beneath the world's oceans. Their ongoing research will become an integral part of the growing body of knowledge in earth sciences, eventually enabling us to put together the pieces of the Earth's puzzling history – its geologic past, present and future.

Chapter 13

Marine Mammals

THE US NAVY began its Marine Mammal Program in 1960 when it acquired a Pacific white-sided dolphin as part of its hydrodynamic studies. Scientists involved with the design of torpedoes and other underwater weapons had reviewed reports on the hydrodynamic efficiency of dolphins, and were keen to investigate them to determine if in fact the dolphins did have special characteristics which could be applied to their design work. A study programme was put together to evaluate the animals' qualities and hydrodynamic capabilities. Little research data or developed techniques were available, which called into question the quality of the results of the programme. It was a topic that remained with the designers and a new programme was developed with the same aims, but more clearly defined. They wanted to know if the dolphin possessed a highly evolved drag-reducing system. Among the possible drag-reducing mechanisms that were studied were the dolphin's skin compliances, biopolymers and boundary layer heating, which may or may not work synergistically. The development of instrumentation for taking the measurements, recording the data and analysing the results made the studies possible.

While scientists viewed the dolphin as a method of improving underwater weapon design, the Navy saw other possibilities, and in 1963 developed research programmes in order that they could study marine mammals' specially developed senses and capabilities, in particular their 'sonar' and their deep diving physiology. They also wanted to know if dolphins and sea-lions could be trained to undertake underwater tasks, either in support of or in place of divers.

The first base for the Navy Marine Mammal research unit was at Point Mugu, California, USA. It was a very modest establishment in terms of research and development, but it was to grow as the programmes developed. The demonstration that trained dolphins and sea-lions could be worked untethered in the open ocean with great reliability was a major achievement.

Some of the most notable progress was made with a Navy dolphin named Tuffy, who participated in the Sealab I and II habitat projects. Tuffy (his original name was Tuf Guy) was part of a dolphin show at an amusement park in Santa Monica, California, USA, when he was transferred to the Navy. He did not fit the normal picture of a friendly dolphin, for he would bite and butt those who cared for and trained him, so there was no problem about his transfer.

This behaviour continued when he first joined the Navy, but changed thanks to the dedication of laboratory technician Deborah Duffield. She worked with Tuffy (his name now shortened) in her spare time to gain his confidence and encourage him to undertake simple tasks. This was so successful that Tuffy was able to begin a full programme of training. A special harness was designed for him and fitted with a device that would transmit depth data to his trainers. This proved valuable in providing a data bank not only of the depth reached, but also of the time spent underwater.

Tuffy's trainers had to establish a recall signal so that he would know

when to return to the surface. They used a small waterproof strobe light similar to that carried by aircrews as part of their survival equipment. The light itself was of little value as it did not penetrate very far through the water, but when the light strobed it caused a click, and it was that sound that Tuffy was trained to respond to. Such was the dolphin's ability that he could easily identify the strobe clicks amidst all the other underwater noises.

In 1965 Tuffy had progressed so far in his training development that he was moved to an ocean pen and undertook his first dive in the open sea, although he was held on a lead. His excursions into the ocean were successful and he was soon able to locate and recover a ring fitted with a pinger in water depths up to 35 m (115 ft). It is worth noting that the ocean pens were large and only protruded out of the water about 0.6 m (2 ft), which meant that Tuffy, or any dolphin, could easily have jumped over at any time and made good their escape.

The following extract, taken from the book *Marine Mammals and Man, The Navy's Porpoises and Sea-lions* by Forrest G. Wood, describes one operation undertaken by another dolphin:

Afloat in the green surf of a top secret cove on the rugged seacoast of California, a 181.5 kg (400 lb) bottlenosed dolphin coolly awaited a special underwater signal. When it came, it would send him quickly in search of a $4,700 missile target booster cradle somewhere at the bottom of the sea. The hunt should take only seconds.

The fastest human diver might take hours. Topside, dozens of naval aides and technicians with stop watches, earphones and clipboards stood by to jot down the results which would add up to one more record in the books for the most tested, measured and coddled creature of the space age . . .

In the east, a glistening object, the missile target, appeared in the hot sky and hurtled seaward. The finning dolphin watched it casually, saw booster and booster cradle fall from the missile target into the ocean, heard a distant splash and gurgle as $4,700 worth of taxpayers' money disappeared in the bay. Then came the sound he had been programmed for, ping-pong-ping, the command to 'seek'.

Down he dived, sleek, rubbery, needle nosed, searching out the sound's source. Topside, his dock crew cheered and pushed pencils. They would report later that he had swum at twenty four knots under water, an incredible speed even for a dolphin.

Clicking and rasping, the bottlenose moved his head from side to side, scanning the clicks echoing back from the target. In seconds, the booster cradle's vague bulk loomed before his eyes, exactly where his sonar apparatus had told him. He threw back his head and tossed off a plastic ring carried on his beak. Immediately a float secured to the ring rose to the surface of the ocean: now, divers could easily follow the line attached to the float and secure the rocket-booster cradle.

Mission completed, the bottlenose whipped around in a tight 180° turn and zoomed back to the dock. When he surfaced, a cheer went up from the waiting crew. His trainer was grinning from ear to ear, holding out his reward, a seventeen cent mullet in exchange for $4,700 worth of space hardware.

Another of Tuffy's operational challenges came with the Sealab I underwater programme. Divers were to be deployed to the habitat for two weeks at a depth of 61 m (200 ft). They would breathe a helium/oxygen gas mixture and be saturated, which means that they would not be able to return to the surface without first undergoing a lengthy period of decompression. The divers were really concerned that they might get lost in the murky water around the habitat and not be able to find their way back to it or return to the surface. The programme that was developed for Tuffy was for him to assist the divers and effect the rescue of a lost diver. This would be achieved by fitting a rescue line on the outside of the habitat. When the diver activated an emergency buzzer, Tuffy would go to the reel and collect a ring, at the end of the line, on his snout and swim to the diver's signal. The diver would take the ring and follow the line back to the habitat. Tuffy's other task would be to carry tools from diver to diver, and back and forth from the divers to the surface.

Tuffy had been trained under controlled conditions, but at the operational site there were major distractions. The support vessel providing power to Sealab required a large and noisy generator,

which transmitted through the water. The habitat was also a distraction with its underwater lights. Tuffy had to adapt to these distractions, but he was soon participating and carried out training diver rescue tasks and ferried tools to and from the divers. The experiment was underfunded, but the result proved beyond doubt that mammals could be trained to participate in man-under-the-sea programmes.

Sealab II was an extension of Sealab I, designed to be operated at a depth of 131 m (430 ft), and it would involve the use of dolphins and sea-lions. Tuffy extended the diver rescue capability during training trials and could locate a diver more than 30.5 m (100 ft) away from the habitat. The Sealab II experiments were delayed, but the training of dolphins and sea-lions continued. The scientists wanted the dolphins to put their heads into the hatch on the underside of the habitat. It had been reported that a wild sea-lion had put its head into the Sealab I hatch and drawn a breath of a heliox mixture. The sea-lion had returned to the surface with no adverse effects. During training the dolphins were encouraged to put their heads into the hatch but they would not breathe. Better results were obtained with the sea-lions and it was proposed that they should be used during the diving operations.

In 1968 there was a change to the Sealab programme and it was decided to set the experiment in 183 m (600 ft) of water. This required some urgent deep diving training, but by 1969 the Sealab II project had been cancelled. Tuffy continued to work on underwater experiments and eventually died of a clostridial infection, but he had established a sound basis for the training of mammals.

During the Sealab training programmes NRaD moved its base from Point Mugu to San Diego, USA, and a laboratory was established in Hawaii. Some of the personnel and animals were transferred to the facility in Hawaii and the rest moved to Point Loma in San Diego. Research continued into the capabilities of marine mammals, including the development of improved techniques for the diagnosis and treatment of health problems. There were neurophysiological studies using behavioural and other non-invasive techniques, to gain a better understanding of how a large dolphin brain functions. Supporting this research was the development of instrumentation for determining brain-wave activity, the hearing range of a dolphin, and how dolphins produce the sounds they make. They also undertook research into the dolphin echo-location system, and were heavily involved in evaluating and developing marine mammals to undertake work tasks which would be more suited to them than to human divers or deep submersibles.

The Marine Mammal Laboratory in Hawaii also developed a programme to train sea-lions to locate and attach a recovery device to objects on the seabed. The first phase of the programme required the employment of California sea-lions, who had to adapt to being handled before the training could begin. They were fitted with a handling harness and a foam Neoprene muzzle. The harness gave the trainers control during transfer and training and the muzzle would stop the animals from hunting for food and provided the attachment point for the recovery device.

Training mammals to carry out work tasks underwater is time-consuming, so when the initial phase is completed, the animals will have reached the point where operational training can commence. This requires the sea-lions to be fitted with a lead so that the trainer retains control. At the end of the lead, the sea-lions descend to depth to locate the source of a pre-positioned pinger. The animals then press a rubber pad to indicate that they have reached the object. All this is undertaken in very controlled conditions and the real test begins when the trainers take their charges to open water.

This phase of the training programme is critical as the animals have to work in open water and, after initial dives, without a lead. They also have to respond to a recall signal. A clamp device was developed which has to be carried in the mouth and the animals are trained to carry it and fit it to an object.

Operationally, this requires the sea-lions to be taken out to sea on a support

vessel where a device, fitted with a pinger, is lowered to the seabed. The sea-lion and trainers transfer to a rubber boat and move away to the general location of the device. The sea-lion then enters the water and descends to the seabed. If the device is located and identified by the pinger, the animal returns to the rubber boat and presses a rubber pad to indicate the find. A clamp device is then fitted, and the sea-lion is deployed into the water again. A line is attached to the clamp and paid out by a trainer as the animal descends. The clamp is pushed against the device so that the two curved arms close around the object. Once the clamp is in place the sea-lion returns to the rubber boat for a reward of fish, leaving the trainers to pull the device to the surface or, if it is too

A sea-lion attaches a snap hook to an object held in the training pen. Once the connection is made the sea-lion returns to the surface and the divers can pull the object up. (US Navy)

piece was designed to fit each of the whales, and was fitted with a clamp device which operated in the same way as those carried by the sea-lions. When the clamp was in place it automatically detached itself from the mouthpiece. The clamp contained a hydrazine gas lifting system which was activated when the mouthpiece was removed. The gas inflated a balloon that was sufficient to lift the object to the surface.

Another major objective of Deep Ops was to determine the depth to which whales can dive. Belugas or white whales were investigated by the NRaD San Diego and Hawaii facilities, who found that belugas are inshore and estuarine animals which enter rivers for calving and feeding and are capable of diving to depths of at least 640.5 m (2,100 ft). A beluga was trained to attach a recovery device to an object at 396.5 m (1,300 ft). This clearly shows the flexibility and adaptability of these great animals.

Morgan, the pilot whale, made a working dive to 228.7 m (750 ft), while Ahab, one of the killer whales, made a descent to 259 m (850 ft) and remained underwater for 7 minutes 40 seconds, which was his deepest dive and longest breath hold. The other killer whale, Ishmael, was taken to the operational worksite and dived as planned, but instead of returning in answer to the recall signal he moved further out to sea. The training team attempted to locate the whale but failed to do so. The team were also concerned about Ahab because his behaviour deteriorated to the point where his diving programme was terminated. Morgan continued to perform and after a number of dives reached 347.7 m (1,140 ft) and eventually achieved his deepest dive of 504.4 m (1,654 ft). This proved to NRaD scientists that pilot whales could undertake search and recovery operations to depths which are at the extreme limits of saturation diving and could cope with all that such an operation would entail.

All Navy maritime mammal training is carried out using positive training measures with food as a reward, which means that animals are rewarded with fish for performing their tasks correctly but they

Bigger objects required bigger clamps and they needed larger and more powerful carriers. The orca or killer whales fitted the bill and they have adapted to the training. Ahab weighs 2,495 kg (5,500 lb) and has no problems with the clamp. He is able to locate the device using an acoustic pinger to guide him. The clamp closes automatically and he then releases it, causing the hydrazine system to actuate and allowing the object to float to the surface. (US Navy)

heavy, to wait for assistance from the larger vessel. Recovery training, from phase one to working at depth, lasts some 15 months.

While dolphins and sea-lions were establishing a creditable record for working underwater, another group was being trained as part of an experimental programme. This project was called Deep Ops and involved a pilot whale and two killer whales, which were to be trained to recover objects from much greater depths.

The pilot whale, named Morgan, adapted to the training quickly, while the killer whales Ahab and Ishmael were less responsive, but all were trained to a point where they were fitted with a harness which was equipped with a radio transmitter for the purpose of locating them if they wandered away. A special mouth-

The killer whale Ishmael returns a grabber device to its trainer after having fitted the clamp to an object on the seabed. The trainer can then fit another clamp before passing it back to the whale for another dive. (US Navy)

are not punished if they fail. This system of training and working has proved effective because without a relationship of trust the dolphins, sea-lions and whales would make good their escape when taken out to sea and released to undertake dives. Statistics show that in the course of 30 years of untethered training only seven dolphins failed to return to their enclosures.

All the research and training programmes undertaken by the US Navy have used captive mammals. Other organizations have studied various groups in the wild, and they have had their own problems. These are well described in a quotation from *Ocean Explorer*, a magazine of the Woods Hole Oceanographic Institution, which states:

If you wanted to study the behaviour and communication of land based wild mammals, you could travel to their habitat, carrying along still and video cameras, a tape recorder, and keen powers of observation. You might sit near a group of chimpanzees for hours at a time, keeping records of everything you saw. If a chimp made a noise, you'd know which chimp it was because you could see it moving as it vocalised. Quickly, you would collect lots of data.

Studying the behaviour of marine mammals, like dolphins, is another kettle of fish. Because they live mostly underwater, coming to the surface usually only to breathe, observations of their behaviour in the wild are fleeting, at best. Most dolphin research has been based on observations made in captivity, at zoos, aquariums, and marine parks. What little is known about dolphins has compelled researchers to want to know more. Dolphins appear to have highly organised societies that are based on long term associations among related females and long term bonds among males. And scientists are beginning to suspect that marine mammals, alone among all other mammals except humans, may be capable of learning vocalisations.

Researchers have studied and will continue to study mammals, and they have developed a range of devices to aid them. The major advances have come from the oceanographic centres under controlled conditions and provide us with valuable information. The knowledge thus gained helps those who take their research into the oceans and seas.

Listening to communications between animals underwater began in the 1950s when Bill Schevill and Bill Watkins of Woods Hole and Barbara Lawrence of

Harvard made the first recordings of whales, using an underwater device developed by Bill Watkins (see below). In the early 1960s, John Lilly, a physician and neurophysiologist, discovered that dolphins had the ability to mimic sounds and considered the possibility that the whistles emitted by dolphins could be 'words'. He went further when he suggested that dolphins could be taught to understand and produce human language. By the mid-1960s and early 1970s David and Melba Caldwell reported upon research which indicated that each dolphin has a 'signature whistle' which is both individual and distinctive. They discovered that the sound made up about 90 per cent of the whistle vocalizations.

Research continued, and by the 1980s Peter Tyack reported that dolphins that live together mimic each other's signature whistles. He suggested that in the wild, this ability might help the dolphins identify each other. It was at this time that Peter Tyack developed the vocalight and the datalogger. Bill Watkins developed a sonar tag which can be attached to the group being studied in the wild, and that provided valuable data on the depth of dives made and recorded the sounds emitted. This very limited profile of dolphin and whale research highlights the fact that it has evolved over a period of more than 40 years. Major advances in underwater technology in recent years may help to speed up these research projects, for as already described, locating the study group is a major exercise in its own right, let alone the problems of following it and collecting data from under the surface of the vast expanses of the oceans and seas.

As mentioned above, credit for 'listening' to whales must go to Bill Watkins and Bill Schevill, who developed an underwater listening device in the 1950s. In its basic form, it was lowered underwater, where it recorded the sounds of the ocean and the creatures living below the surface. It was one thing to listen to the sounds, but quite another to identify their source, and so in 1962, in another first, they developed and began using radio tags. These radio tags were small as they had originally been designed for tracking

pigeons, but they only worked when the whales were on the surface.

From those humble beginnings biologists from the Woods Hole Oceanographic Institution succeeded during 1991 in tracking two whales in the wild and while they were underwater. This has enormous implications for future behavioural studies of mammals in general and whales in particular. The story of their success is quoted from the *Woods Hole Currents* publication.

Using a newly developed sonar tag, biologists from the Woods Hole Oceanographic Institution (WHOI) have succeeded in tracking two whales in the wild under water, an unprecedented achievement with enormous implications for the behavioural study of the world's largest mammals.

'Now we can follow the dives of whales and see what they really do under water,' said WHOI biologist Bill Watkins. The behaviour of whales under water – including their feeding and resting habits, social interactions and even the depth of their dives – is almost entirely unknown.

The new tags were tested in October 1991 on two sperm whales off Dominica in the south eastern Caribbean. The sonar tag, developed by Watkins, is essentially a transponder, a small tube of electronics that emits pulses of sound when electronically interrogated. The tag is thrown from a ship or helicopter so that it attaches to the surface tissue of a whale's back, where it stays for a few weeks, like a splinter in human skin, until it works itself free. The sounds from the tag are received by a ship based laboratory and displayed on a sonar screen, giving the direction, depth and distance of the whale from the ship. One of the most difficult aspects of studying whales is following them, because they spend so much time underwater.

It is obvious that ocean research is a time-consuming business and requires the sort of dedication portrayed by Bill Schevill and Bill Watkins, who discovered in 1977 that the sperm whale has its own pattern of clicks. Peter Tyack, Karen More and Bill Watkins took earlier research further when they analysed 4,000 hours of underwater recordings of finback whales. They discovered that every whale produced different sequences of sound and, even more interestingly, that no whale ever repeated itself. This research was extended to include humpback whales and they too were found never to repeat their song the same way twice. The problems encountered by this research are best summarized by quoting again from the *Woods Hole Currents* publication.

It appears that humans and cetaceans are the only animals who can learn a vocal identity, that is, a signature sound unique to a single individual.

Also, some species of whales and porpoises can imitate sounds, a talent they share only with humans, four families of birds, and Hoover, an extraordinary seal.

What are these animals actually communicating? Some sounds appear to be what the biologists call 'shared vocalisations,' such as: hello, go away, get out of my way. During breeding season, many male whales, including humpbacks and finbacks, which are among the most studied, advertise themselves to females with their songs. The breeding song of the humpback changes every year; indeed, the song changes from week to week during one season. Perhaps, some biologists speculate, one male begins to sing and the other males in the group pick up the tune. Which whales decide to improvise and why? And how does the lead singer decide what song to sing?

'We don't really know,' Tyack said. 'We've never been able to follow individual singers much longer than a day. Whales are very difficult to follow.'

The quotation refers to 'Hoover, an extraordinary seal'. Hoover's story is interesting. He was a harbour seal who upon becoming an orphan was adopted by a Mr Swallow. Hoover remained at the Swallows' home until he grew too large and he then took up residence at an aquarium. Seven years later, when Peter Tyack of the WHOI was visiting the aquarium, he passed the seal enclosure and heard someone speak. His first reaction was that someone had fallen into the seal pool but upon investigation he found

Hoover. He had heard the words 'Hello they-ah! Come ova heeah!'. There were other distinct phrases such as 'Hey! Get outta theyah' and 'Hoover, Hoova'. While the speech was distinct it was not something that those concerned wanted publicized and it was unique in that no other sea creature could mimic human sounds. Tyack visited Mr Swallow and formed the opinion that not only did Hoover speak human words but he did so with an accent that was identical to Mr Swallow's. If there is more to the story it will never be known, for it passed into the annals of history when Hoover died of old age several years ago.

Peter Tyack has studied dolphins for some 15 years and must be considered a leading exponent in dolphin research. His work required studies to be made of both wild and captured dolphins, the former proving to be a difficult task. The best option for basic research and for the development of equipment to do it with was with dolphins which were close at hand and so could be studied in detail. A research centre with readily available resources was the Seven Seas Panorama at Brookfield Zoo, Chicago, USA.

He knew that dolphins emitted whistles but did not know how those whistles compared when two dolphins were kept together. The problem was, that if two dolphins whistled together he could not identify which had made which whistle. This was compounded by the fact that humans are not able readily to identify sound direction underwater.

To overcome this problem he designed the 'vocalight', which was attached to the dolphin's head using a suction cup and lit up when the dolphin made a sound. It was also designed to react to noise, so that the louder the sound, the more lights flashed. For identification purposes, one set of lights was red and the other green. Underwater microphones recorded the whistles for correlation of lights and sound.

From the results which were obtained by the study it was determined that 90 per cent of the sounds emitted by one dolphin were of his own signature and the remaining 10 per cent were virtually a mimic of the other dolphin's whistles. The same results were found when examining the other dolphin's whistles.

To take the project to the open sea and undertake research in the wild would be more difficult, so he designed the acoustic datalogger. This device is also attached by a suction cup, and houses a microcomputer that can store information. Apart from obtaining data on how loud certain sounds are, it records sound frequency.

While research continues into communications between dolphins, another aspect of research is being conducted by Amy Samuels, who is a specialist in non-verbal communication. She also uses the facilities at the Seven Seas Panorama at Brookfield Zoo, Chicago. Most researchers study dolphins in groups, which causes identification problems in the wild. In fact it is the dorsal fin which provides the identification as this is distinctive to each dolphin, but it is no easy task to spot one fin among many in a group which surfaces. Amy's response to this was to study one animal in detail by a method called 'focal animal sampling'. This requires hours of concentrated study, and recording all body movements no matter how subtle. It is in fact a look into the private life of a dolphin. To further enhance this research it was important to know how the internal functions of the body corresponded to the external movements. This has been achieved by the staff of the Seven Seas Panorama through the development of a new non-invasive technique for monitoring the reproductive hormones of dolphins by taking samples of saliva rather than blood. These are the techniques that Amy Samuels uses for her part of the study of these beautiful and intelligent creatures, who appear to be closer to human beings than we had imagined.

The Whale Conservation Institute

Whales are also of great interest to The Whale Conservation Institute (WCI), and they have a very active research study programme whose special problems require special equipment. Iain Kerr of the WCI describes (courtesy of WHOI) the hurdles facing the researchers as well as their accomplishments:

How on earth do you study a whale like the sperm whale? A whale that swims at five knots, dives to depths exceeding a mile, and holds its breath for over two hours?

Well, the first thing you do is get yourself a research platform that can handle fair, foul, and fouler weather. You then fund the programme and get the proper permits, fight off scores of desperate young scientists that are trying to make the best of their education on your vessel, and last but not least, you dash madly to Benthos to get some decent equipment.

Cetaceans are acoustic animals relying, in most cases, on sound rather than sight to interpret their world. To better understand these mammals and to determine their critical habitat, it is necessary to spend extended periods of time with them observing their behaviour, which is not an easy task. The WCI turned to a world leader in undersea and remote sensing technology, Benthos, to provide the specialist equipment they needed:

In 1989, we purchased two Benthos AQ-13 hydrophones and constructed our own two channel array. This array can be towed at speeds up to 15 knots. We have a directional capability due to the delay time of the sounds arriving at each hydrophone, and by incorporating the correct filters, we can even hear whales up to 9.6 km (6 miles) away when we are underway all above the noise of our main engine.

We have dragged our Benthos acoustic array well over 32,180 km (20,000 miles) since 1989, and it is still going strong. We are now looking for ways to size sperm whales acoustically. When you add this to the fact that we can determine approximately where the animals are, what size group they are travelling in, their sex, and sometimes even what they are doing just by listening to their vocalisations, this array is an invaluable research tool.

WCI has one of the largest cetacean libraries in the world, with over 5,000 hours of humpback whale recordings alone. Recordings are even carried as part of the payload aboard the *Voyager I* and *II* spacecraft and were used in the films *Hunt for Red October* and *Star Trek IV: The Voyage Home.*

Observing whales and dolphins is not restricted to the large and official institutes. Individuals can now take part in specialist holiday programmes of dolphin and whale watching. The UK Whale and Dolphin Conservation Society has combined with a specialist travel company, Discover the World, to produce a range of exclusive tailor-made holidays to all parts of the world. It is an important fact that, apart from taking small groups to study and view these magnificent creatures, a considerable proportion of the income from every trip goes to the Society, to support its work around the world. The scope of programmes available is comprehensive and includes a weekend dolphin watch in Gibraltar, a land-based trip to see right whales in South Africa and a chance to kayak through the gray whale breeding lagoons of Mexico. There is a weekend to watch killer whales off the rugged south coast of Iceland or whale watching in Japan. Those who admire dolphins and seek closer contact with them can swim with spotted dolphins in the crystal-clear waters of the Bahamas. Perhaps those who can afford to take these opportunities will then themselves get more involved in the exploration and preservation of our oceans and seas, for that is a task for every individual.

Chapter 14

Exploiting Undersea Minerals

OIL AND GAS reservoirs generally occur in certain types of area and structure and an oil exploration company will need to gather and interpret the kind of information that will indicate locations that may produce hydrocarbons. The areas where hydrocarbons are likely to be discovered are extremely large and so require a very detailed survey to determine the exact locations that warrant exploration drilling.

The most widely used geophysical method of exploration, and the one that provides the most detail, is the seismic survey. The system works by initiating shock-waves on the surface either by explosive charge or by high-frequency sound; the same effect can be achieved by using a compressed air gun, which is cheaper and does not affect marine life. The sound-waves travel down through the sea and earth and are then reflected back to the surface from deep rock strata of differing properties. The reflected waves are recorded by sensitive measuring instruments called hydrophones that are located on the surface of the water. The speed of the sound-waves is known and the time of the reflections can be measured, so determining the depth of each reflecting layer. The intensity of the reflection is correlated to rock composition. Survey work is vital as considerable sums of money will be expended if the companies decide to drill exploration wells in the search for oil or gas.

To recover oil from below our seas requires special drilling units, termed 'mobile drilling units' (MDUs), of which there are three categories. In shallower waters, 'jack-up' drilling rigs have legs which rest on the seabed when the rig is drilling a well, and are raised up clear to allow the rig to be towed to another location once the job is finished. In deeper water, 'semi submersible' drilling rigs offer a floating unit, which is anchored to hold it in place. Most semi subs are square-shaped with two large pontoons, with large columns supporting the main body of the rig. The design of these units provides a stable platform, even during rough weather. In the deep and more remote areas where the drilling unit has to sail to a location, drill ships are available. These take the shape of a conventional ship, and have the drilling tower in the centre of the vessel. They hold station using dynamic positioning.

Each of these units is able to remain in position and drill down to thousands of metres. When oil and gas are located, they are under pressure and the flow must be

A 'jack-up' drilling rig requires the base of its legs to rest on the seabed. Because the rigs are generally deployed in shallower water, with strong currents, the base of the legs can scour, making the rig unstable. If this occurs, divers are required to install a stabilizing system to eliminate the problems.

controlled while geologists study the 'find' to determine the extent of the field. To complete this, a number of holes may need to be drilled at different locations. If the field is large and financially viable, it is developed by the establishment of fixed platforms. These can take the form of steel-legged jackets or concrete bases with the platform facilities fitted on top. These platforms are self-sufficient developments set in a remote and often hostile environment.

The first drilling rigs arrived in the southern North Sea in the early 1960s and began exploration drilling. It was in 1965 that the first commercial discovery of gas was made. Rapid development of other fields followed and pipelines were laid to carry the gas ashore. Exploration continued and moved north where deposits of oil were discovered, with the first commercially viable field being found in 1969. Almost a year later, one of the largest UK oilfields was discovered, but the largest North Sea field has been made in the Norwegian sector.

A major problem which has always affected oil and gas exploration and production in the North Sea and continues today is the weather and sea states. They can accurately be described as the worst in the world where hydrocarbons are

Surveyors will determine the exact location of a new platform. When the barge is in position, the launch process begins and the steel structure slides from the barge into the sea. After final adjustments of position the bottom end is sunk. Once on location the structure is secured to the seabed before the process of construction of the topside begins. (Gordon Clark)

exploited offshore. Strong seabed currents which pass underwater structures cause scouring, leaving holes. This is particularly worrying in the case of pipelines, as the scouring action removes the seabed causing sections of pipe to be unsupported. This can exceed the design criteria and, if not corrected, can lead to critical damage to the pipeline. These problems are generally confined to the shallower southern sector, but in the north, structures have to endure and bear the brunt of another particular weather problem. Offshore structures must be able to withstand the severest weather, the 100-year storm. This is the storm which is deemed to occur once every 100 years, and because of it platforms have to be designed to withstand 30 m (100 ft) waves, a sustained wind force of 190 km/h (120 mph) and wind gusts of short duration up to 250 km/h (160 mph).

Offshore oil and gas production platforms are sited over wells through which the hydrocarbons flow, from the reservoirs deep below the seabed to the processing plant on the platform. Once the oil and gas have been gathered, they have to be transported ashore and for the vast majority of oil and gas fields, that requires pipelines. The pipelines, which often extend for several hundred kilometres, vary in size up to 1 m (39 in) in diameter. They all have to be laid, and once in place they are susceptible to damage.

There are two types of pipeline which carry hydrocarbons, of which the rigid steel ones are in the majority and carry oil or gas over long lengths. Flexible pipelines are generally used for short runs, between platforms and underwater wellheads, or between two platforms. Flexible pipelines are carried to the work site on large reels on the stern of a vessel and are in a continuous length. The laying vessel will have dynamic positioning and deploy the pipe by reeling it off. Divers then connect the ends to other pipelines or connecting points using flanges, which are bolted together. Advantages with the flexible pipe are that it can be laid quickly, it is cost-effective and it can be recovered to be used again.

Rigid steel pipe lengths are welded together as they are laid. This operation is undertaken by a special vessel called a 'lay barge', where lengths of basic steel tubes start at one end of the barge and leave the other end welded together, the welds tested, and the pipe coated with a protective coating. The laying operation is a continuous process which leaves the completed pipeline lying on the seabed. It can then be buried by a seabed burial device such as those described in Chapter 11, to protect it from damage which could be caused by ships' anchors or fishing vessels' trawls.

Pipelines are laid as close as possible to platforms, but they need to be connected to the riser (a pipe which extends from the platform's production system to the seabed), and that can be accomplished by welding the two together using a special technique called 'hyperbaric welding'. Divers can wet weld underwater but the weld itself is not of a suitable standard for use on pipelines. To meet the exacting standards of welds carried out on the surface, the underwater weld must be done in the dry. The hyperbaric weld is an accepted part of the offshore hydrocarbon industry and today is a refined skill of specialist welder divers.

Hyperbaric welding operations begin with the two ends of the pipeline being prepared by divers. This requires handling frames to be placed over either end of the pipeline, enabling it to be lifted clear of

An underwater pipeline which requires a repair may need to be hyperbaric welded. This would need a clean cut, undertaken by machine. A cutter is installed by a diver and is hydraulically powered. It is able to complete a bevelled edge cut. (Alain Tocco, Comex)

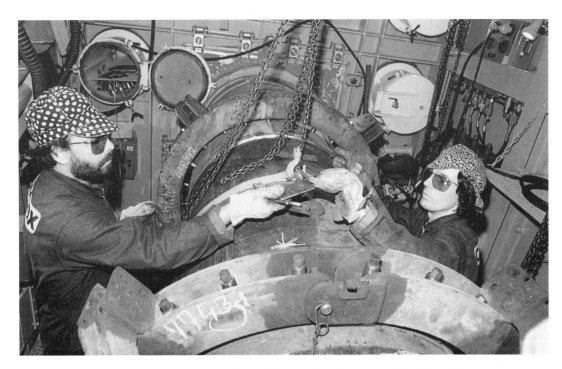

Inside the habitat the welder divers have removed their diving equipment and prepare the two ends of the pipeline for a hyperbaric weld. (Alain Tocco, Comex)

the seabed and the two sections aligned. When these basic preparations are completed a habitat is lowered and placed over the place to be welded. A slot at either end of the habitat allows it to seal around the pipe. When the seal is secure, gas is delivered from the surface support vessel through the habitat's umbilical. This pushes the water out, leaving a gas pressure inside equal to that of the surrounding water pressure.

Access to the habitat by the welders can be undertaken by a specially adapted bell which mates directly onto the habitat, allowing a dry transfer for the welder divers. If there is no dry transfer facility, the normal bell can be lowered alongside the habitat and the welders have to lock out of the bell as for a conventional dive and swim or walk across to the habitat and enter it from the underside. When the latter option is selected (as is most often the case), the welders remove their diving helmets and can exchange their diving suits for overalls. An umbilical passes between the surface support vessel and the habitat. It provides gas supply and return hoses, communications cables, electrical power cables and television cables. The support vessel therefore has to remain on station throughout the entire operation.

When the habitat is established and

ready, the specialized welding equipment is prepared. The ends of the pipe are cut clean and bevelled, ready for welding. The weld area is then demagnetized and preheated using electrically powered heating pads prior to the weld being undertaken. When the weld is completed, it is subjected to radiographic examination to check its integrity. Once the weld is passed, the exposed section is wrapped with bitumen tape to seal it and complete the operation. The habitat is flooded with water and recovered to the surface support vessel. The pipeline is then lowered back to the seabed, and the handling frames are recovered. A protective covering can then be laid over the pipeline which can take the form of specially designed mattresses, burial by a plough or seabed tractor, or by dumping stone over it.

The Dutch company Van Oord ACZ are world leaders in a wide range of capabilities. Stabilizing, protecting and covering pipelines, flowlines and cables offers a rapid intervention system to protect them from anchors and fishing equipment. Holes caused by the scouring of the seabed around platforms, rigs and structures can be filled as part of stabilization and remedial projects.

Ballasting operations were first developed using a vessel with doors in the bottom of the hull. When the vessel was in position over the work site, the doors were opened and the ballast dropped to the seabed. It was at best a hit-and-miss system, especially in deeper water where the stone would spread out, covering a large area. This method was not cost-effective, particularly for dedicated pipeline or cable work.

The solution required some innovative thinking and resulted in Van Oord ACZ developing a ballasting system and specially adapted vessels to meet expanding requirements. It was determined that particular size stone was required for specific projects so that engineers could obtain the most effective coverage. Putting the ballast where it was required and not spreading it over a wide area of the seabed was also a vital aspect which needed developing. The answer was a flexible fall pipe system, which could extend to a depth of 600 m (1,968 ft). The tube is constructed in a chain-mail fashion which allows it to be lowered and raised easily. One metre (3.2 ft) in diameter, it allows the ballast to fall to the seabed in a controlled manner.

On board the vessel a unique conveyor belt system carries the ballast from the hold above the upper deck to the feed point where it is deposited into the tube. In order that all of the ballast in the holds can be reached and used there is a system of conveyor control. The displacement of the ballast is also a critical factor in the stability of the vessel. To complete the overall system and to both control the placement and ensure coverage, a specially designed remote operated vehicle is incorporated at the end of the tube. This ROV is of a tubular design and has the ballast passing through its centre. Powerful lights and television cameras illuminate and provide visual coverage of the operation. Sub-sea sonar systems pass information on the target's location to the plotting system on the bridge to feed data into the vessel's autotrack unit. They also provide data to the engineers whose task it is to ensure that the work is carried out according to the requirements of the programme. The ROV pilots can use the vehicle's thrusters to provide a limited amount of movement of the tube during ballasting operations, and it can also be used for pre-site surveys and to survey upon completion.

With the development of offshore oil and gas fields throughout the world there are a lot of pipelines and cables to be buried and protected. That means that the

Figure 17: *The flexible fall pipe vessel* Tertness, *showing the rock-dumping configuration.* (Van Oord ACZ)

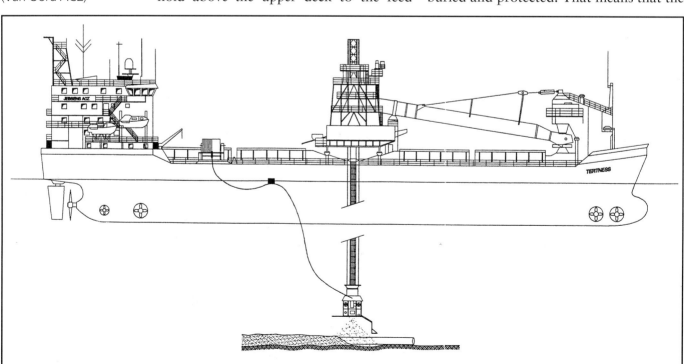

Van Oord ACZ fleet of flexible fall pipe vessels undertake large- and small-scale operations throughout the world. One project involved the 134 km (83.2 mile) pipeline which runs between the North Ramkin 'A' platform and the onshore treatment plant in Western Australia. A survey had found that sections of the pipeline had become exposed as a result of cyclonic weather conditions. The first phase of the operation was undertaken between March and May 1991 using the flexible fall pipe vessel *Trollness* to dump some 175,000 tons of small rock material to provide a filter layer over the pipeline. The second phase was undertaken in September and October of the same year using the vessel *Rocky Giant*, which dumped armour rock on top of the filter layer. This was so successful that five additional projects were added, extending the rock dumping operations until February 1992, by which time a total quantity of approximately 400,000 tons of rock had been placed on the seabed.

In 1992 the *Rocky Giant* moved to New Zealand where there was a 15 km (9.3 mile) pipeline between the Maui 'A' and Maui 'B' platforms. This project required the vessel to work in the notoriously rough Tasman Sea, off the Taranaki coast, between April and October 1992. The ballast was small in size and required a special semi-closed fall pipe to be produced to ensure that the material could be contained. The dumping was conducted in a water depth of 110 m (360 ft) and deposited approximately 200,000 tons of material.

For marginal oilfield development it may not be cost-effective to lay a pipeline from the oilfield to the shore, so there needs to be an effective alternative. The best option is to load the oil straight into a tanker, in the field, so that it can be taken direct to a refinery. To load a tanker at sea requires a mooring buoy anchored at a fixed point which is capable of holding the tanker while it is being loaded. The oil is transported through a pipeline from the platform to a manifold under the buoy. Flexible hoses span the distance between the manifold and the buoy. The tanker is attached to the buoy by a mooring line,

the buoy being designed to rotate to allow the tanker to lie with the current or wind direction. Floating hoses span the final gap between the buoy and the tanker. Control of the oil flow is undertaken on the platform, but the tanker can slip the hoses by dropping them into the sea and can release itself from the buoy in an emergency or in extreme weather conditions.

Another option is to have a tanker permanently attached to a single point mooring system where it remains to be used as a storage facility. This allows for oil to flow continually into the storage tanker, to then be transferred to a mobile tanker which will carry it to the onshore facility. Storage tankers have also been developed to become production vessels, undertaking with the additional equipment the role

The Van Oord ACZ flexible fall pipe vessel Rocky Giant *in operation. The fall pipe tower can be seen on the starboard side of the vessel. A large hopper is replenished by two cranes which transfer stone from the holds into the hopper. From there the stone is conveyed to the top of the fall tube. The rate of flow is controlled at the unit with guidance from the ROV pilot who is able to monitor progress via the underwater television cameras. (Van Oord ACZ)*

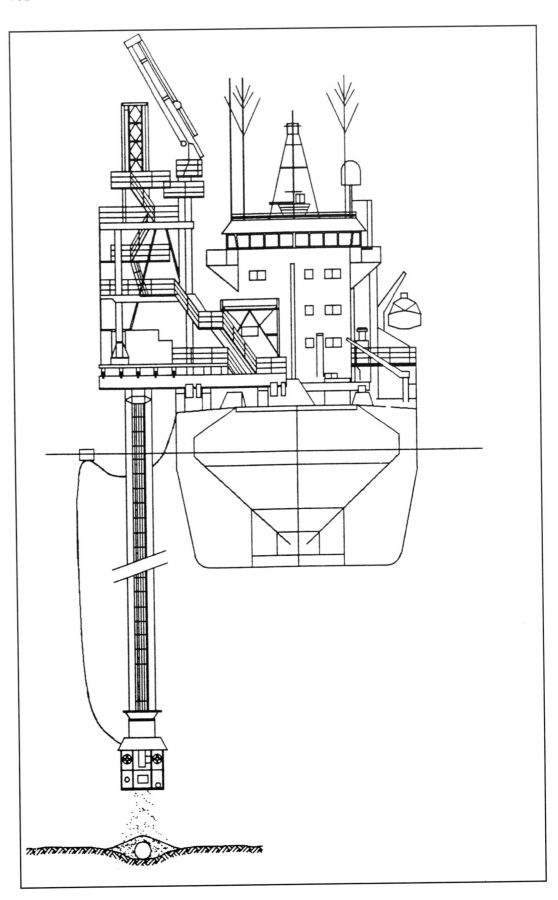

Figure 18: *The flexible fall pipe vessel* Tertness, *showing the side launch structure, fall pipe and ROV used for rock dumping.* (Van Oord ACZ)

of the production platform. This is a cost-effective option for marginal fields where a conventional platform would be uneconomic.

The search for oil in the North Sea means working on average in water depths of 122 m (400 ft), which means that some areas are shallower than that and others are deeper. Exploiting the deeper areas has required major advances in sub-sea technology. It is these advances that will make it possible for companies to exploit an oilfield in some 1,830 m (6,000 ft) of water in the Gulf of Mexico. Undertaking a project of this magnitude, with all the associated technical problems that will have to be overcome, is beyond the capabilities of one company. As a result, a consortium has been set up headed by Texaco with 11 other major oil companies participating in the project and pooling their knowledge and experience.

In the North Sea, divers work in 122 m (400 ft) of water every day, and under controlled and simulated conditions they have worked at 475 m (1,558 ft). This new project will be undertaken in a water depth of 1.6 km (1 mile). The technical challenges facing the consortium will stretch the project team, because while the

basic knowledge needed may already be available, much will have to be developed to function at this depth. Wells will have to be drilled – no mean feat as 1,830 m (6,000 ft) of drill pipe will have to be lowered before the actual drilling process begins. Once the wells are prepared, wellheads will be placed on the wells and then connected to a satellite sub-sea system manifold by pipelines. These all have to be capable of enduring considerable internal and external pressures because of the depth involved. The wellheads and manifolds will have to be installed without the aid of divers. There are manned submersibles and ROVs capable of working at this depth, but considerable research and development will be needed to prepare tool packages to make them cost-effective and efficient. Another major problem facing the project team will be the installation of the pipelines and electrical control cables between the manifolds in 1,830 m (6,000 ft) of water and the platforms in 183 m (600 ft). To compound the problem of working at these depths, there is the actual extraction of the oil itself. It will flow under pressure to the wellhead, but it will then have to be transported more than 96.5 km (60 miles)

A diving support vessel backs up to the single anchor leg of a floating production and storage facility. The connecting arm between the leg on the right and the tanker not only holds the tanker in position but also carries the pipes through which the oil travels. By using this system of oil recovery, the tanker can be moved away and the leg dismantled when the field is no longer productive. (Gordon Clark)

along and 1.6 km (1 mile) up. The UK oil and gas industry has experience of such operations in shallower waters, and once it extends that experience to deep water it will open up new areas for exploration and production.

Pollution

Pollution in the world's oceans and seas is a major problem for today and one that is of great concern for the future. Often, modern pollution is hidden from view beneath the waters' surface, but one that is both visible, far-reaching and has devastating consequences is when an oil tanker with a full cargo of oil products meets with a disaster. There have been recent incidents where tankers have struck coastlines and been broken up by pounding seas, spewing their cargo into the surrounding sea, with some carried on the surface by the currents, and some depositing itself on the seabed. The clean-up operations will fight the disasters on the shore and on the water surface, but below, unseen, the damage is devastating. The ecological balance that makes up the undersea world is destroyed, with far-reaching consequences, a situation that the vast majority of people are totally unaware of. While disasters do happen, all is not always lost, and two examples show how innovation, determination and underwater engineering skills combine to create a vital salvage system which not only saves our seas but can reduce the financial loss.

The *Boehlen*, an (East) German tanker, sank in October 1976 off Finistere, some 65 km (35 nautical miles) from Brest, France. It had a cargo of thick viscous crude oil which had been loaded in Venezuela, South America. An initial survey found that the ship had settled upright on the bottom in 110 m (361 ft) of water. The hull was cracked, allowing 10–15 cu m (13–19 cu yd) of oil to seep into the sea each day, causing a spread of pollution. It was estimated that some 3,000 tonnes of oil remained in 24 tanks.

Français du Petrole sought to stop the leak and remove the oil and engaged Comex to undertake the operations. At their headquarters in Marseilles, France, Comex planned the programme and developed a procedure that would allow the heavy crude to be recovered. The first task was to deploy divers into the oily water to seal the leak and reduce the loss. They then had to tap into the tanks that contained oil, and because the crude was so heavy it had to be heated to make it flow. This was achieved by pumping hot water from the surface support vessel, a drill ship, into the tanks. This made the oil fluid enough to allow it to be pumped up to the drill ship, which had the facilities to control the flow of oil, and in this case it was burnt off. It was not a simple operation and it took four months to complete, involving Comex divers in some 261 bell dives.

The experience gained on the *Boehlen* project gave Comex the vital edge when the *Tanio*, a tanker of 22,000 tonnes, broke in two and sank off Roscoff in 1980. The ensuing pollution created by the release of some 8,000 tonnes of crude oil caused devastation to 30 km (18.6 miles) of the Breton coastline. A careful examination of the wreck, in oil-filled water, was undertaken to determine its exact state. It was discovered that the oil which had leaked into the sea had come from the stern section. The tanks in the bow section, containing some 8,000 tonnes of viscous crude oil, remained intact. The wreck had settled in 94 m (308 ft) of sea water.

This operation was to differ from that of the *Boehlen* in that the salvaged oil could not be burned off because of atmospheric pollution problems. Comex engineers and divers worked on a plan which involved tapping into the oil tanks and recovering the oil to a tanker on the surface. A buoy 120 m (393 ft) long and weighing 700 tonnes was constructed. It was positioned in the sea with the base close to the wreck. Hoses were then connected between the wreck and the buoy's base. The buoy itself had pipes travelling inside to the surface and would transport the oil from the base. A tanker was moored to the buoy and flexible hoses travelled the final section between the buoy and the tanker.

The Comex operation to recover oil from the wreck of the Tanio. *It took 14 months to complete the operation due to atrocious weather conditions. The system used a single leg buoy attached to a base on the seabed. A tanker was moored to the buoy and flexible hoses carried the oil from the wreck to the tanker on the surface. Throughout the operation divers were deployed to set up and maintain the system, which enabled 8,000 tonnes of oil to be salvaged.* (Alain Tocco, Comex)

When all the connections were made, pressurized hot water was pumped from the surface into the hull and the thinned oil was pumped up to the tanker. The success of the operation proved the professional capabilities of all those involved in an operation that took 14 months to complete, often in terrible weather conditions. It saved further pollution of both sea and atmosphere, and managed to save some of the cargo.

Because of the success of the *Boehlen* and *Tanio* salvage operations the French Petroleum Institute and Comex, Marseilles, have joined forces to form an association that will be able to draw upon expertise to combat similar disasters. It is to be hoped that there will never be a disaster of this type again, but realistically, when there is, there is some satisfaction in knowing that expertise is available which could significantly reduce the results of a catastrophe.

Chapter 15

Dynamic Positioning

DYNAMIC POSITIONING MAY be best described as a system which allows a ship to maintain her position and heading automatically, exclusively by means of active thrust. In simple terms this means the use of propellers and thrusters to maintain position. The first vessels to use this technique were the core-drilling vessels *Eureka* and *Caldrill* in 1961. An earlier vessel, the *Cuss 1*, had used a form of dynamic positioning but with manual control of the propellers, but all later vessels used increasingly sophisticated computers to handle the control function. In a sense, dynamic positioning was 'invented' about 100 years ago by the French author Jules Verne, in his novel *Propeller Island*. Reality, of course, had to await the levels of technology unavailable in the 19th century.

From these small beginnings in the 1960s, DP has expanded to encompass over 300 vessels world-wide, including such diverse types as tankers, cable-layers, survey vessels, dive support ships, mine countermeasures vessels, ro-ro ferries, pipelay barges, floating production vessels, crane barges and others. DP is frequently used in shallow waters as well as deep – wherever there is a need for precision station-keeping or manoeuvring. DP has revolutionized the offshore oil and gas industry and has facilitated the exploration of many parts of the oceans where for reasons of harsh environment or adverse conditions, commercial exploitation would not otherwise have been possible.

Dynamic positioned diving support vessels have to work close to platforms, in spite of the fact that the structures are often linked and have sections off at angles, all of which restricts the access. This view shows the helideck on the bow, an integral part of modern diving support vessels to allow crew change and the resupply of urgent stores. (Alain Tocco, Comex)

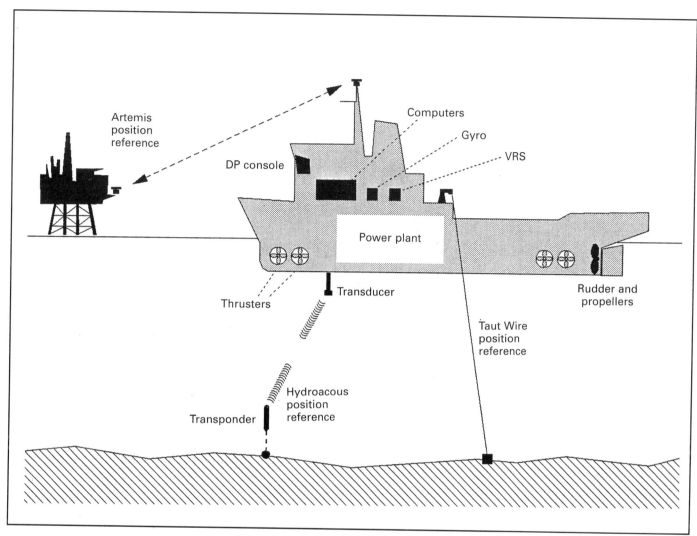

Artemis position reference

DP console

Computers

Gyro

VRS

Power plant

Thrusters

Transducer

Rudder and propellers

Taut Wire position reference

Hydroacous position reference

Transponder

A vessel having a DP capability must be provided with the right mix of hardware, software and personnel expertise. For the more critical high-risk operations a sufficient level of redundancy must be built in to ensure the reliability of the system. The DP system will need to be integrated with other shipboard systems and may rely heavily on external sources of data and monitoring.

Any DP system will consist of six main elements: Computers and Control, Position Reference, Heading Reference, Environment Reference, Power Management and Distribution, and Manoeuvring Systems. It will rely heavily upon computers to handle the large quantity of data and calculation necessary. A continuous comparison has to be made between the 'Set Point' position and heading (i.e. the Desired values) and the Feedback (Measured) values. Raw data about the position of the ship and her heading is collected and processed. Position may be measured simultaneously by a variety of position reference systems, and filtering of the data is necessary to ensure a constant 'best-fit' estimate of the second-to-second position of the vessel. Mathematical modelling techniques allow the prediction of future movements and positions, and the determination of the most economic thruster configuration to maintain the vessel on (or return her to) her set point. The mathematical model contained within the computer is a representation of the vessel and all the features which affect her manoeuvring: mass, wetted surface area, sail (superstructure) area and disposition, thruster characteristics, reaction to wind, waves and current. For vessels where the consequences of the loss of station-keep-

Figure 19: *A DP installation. Dynamic positioned diving support vessels have made deep saturation diving viable in a wide range of applications. DP requires a number of systems which work together to keep a vessel on a predetermined position for an indefinite period of time.* (David Bray)

ing (or 'run-off') would be critical, the computer system may be duplicated or triplicated as a safeguard.

In any DP system it is essential that information regarding the position of the vessel is fed into the computer continually. This position reference needs to be accurate: ideally better than one metre. A variety of systems may be used depending upon circumstances, and the DP system is able to accept inputs from three or more position reference systems simultaneously. In this latter case a 'weighting' or bias factor is applied to each one to reflect its accuracy, allowing the DP to continually use the best possible fit of position. The three most commonly used position reference systems (PRS) at present are Taut Wire, Artemis, and Hydro-Acoustic Position Reference (HPR).

Taut Wire is a mechanical PRS consisting of a small electrically and hydraulically operated crane located on deck. A weight of around half a tonne is placed on the seabed and the wire is kept in tension by the electric motor drive. Once located, the angle of the wire is monitored by a sensor head on the crane jib, and this together with the length of wire deployed will define the position of the vessel relative to the weight. The Taut Wire system is accurate, reliable and self-contained. It is, however, limited in terms of water depth and horizontal range, and yields a relative rather than a geographical position. Many DP vessels are fitted with two Taut Wire systems, one on each side of the vessel.

HPR is a commercial system for locating and tracking underwater objects, work sites or vehicles. One of its many functions is as a position reference for DP ships. The system consists of a probe extending about 4 m (15 ft) below the hull of the vessel. The probe contains a transducer which projects acoustic signals into the water. On the seabed is a transponder which detects the signals and transmits a reply. The reply is detected by the probe and processed in a transceiver unit within the vessel. The distance is determined as an analogue of the measured time-lapse, while the direction whence the reply originated is determined by the transducer head using Ultra-Short Baseline (USBL)

techniques. A display screen shows the positions of the vessel and the transponders interrogated. If the transponder is in a fixed location, then the system becomes a position reference system for the vessel, and the output is usable for DP purposes. Transponders may be laid by the vessel or located upon seabed hardware (wellheads, etc.). Alternatively, a transponder may be located on an ROV (Remotely Operated Vehicle), unmanned submersible or seabed tractor vehicle, allowing the vessel to track or follow the vehicle. HPR is frequently used in vessel DP installations, being accurate, reliable and having a moderate range. Its drawbacks include interference from noise and aeration sub-sea, and it has severe limitations in shallow water.

Artemis is a microwave position reference system consisting of two main installations: the Mobile station and antenna on board ship, and the Fixed station and antenna located upon a nearby platform or other fixed point. Each station consists of a transceiver connected to a 1.5 m (5 ft) slotted waveguide (radar-type) antenna. When in use, a microwave link is established between the two antennae which automatically lock on to one another, training left/right to maintain lock. Signals are continuously transmitted in the 10 GHz band from the Mobile station; these signals are received and retransmitted by the Fixed station, and finally received back again at the ship, with range proportional to time lapse. The bearing or direction is measured at the Fixed station, and transmitted as part of the reply.

Like HPR and Taut Wire, Artemis is a frequently used DP PR system. It is fitted in many vessels, and many North Sea platforms carry at least one Fixed Artemis station and antenna. The system is accurate to 0.5 m (1.64 ft) or better, with a long range up to 5 km (3 miles) for DP purposes. Its drawbacks are that it is susceptible to heat and precipitation interference, loss of signal due to line-of-sight problems, and interference from platform personnel, and it needs platform personnel to assist with setting up. It is, however, capable of giving geographical position reference, since the Fixed station is almost

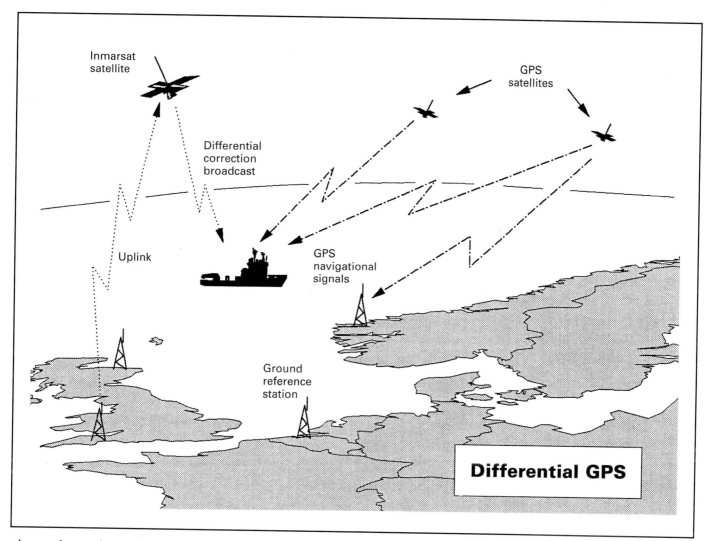

Inmarsat
satellite

GPS
satellites

Differential
correction
broadcast

Uplink

GPS
navigational
signals

Ground
reference
station

Differential GPS

always located at a known geographical point.

Many different position reference systems have been used with DP with varying success. Some of them are based upon radio signals transmitted from fixed locations, giving a hyperbolic or range–range fixing principle. Among these are Argo, Pulse/8, Syledis and Hyperfix. Other systems are laser-based (e.g. Fanbeam) or use satellite transmissions, like the Differential Global Positioning Systems (DGPS). Radactor uses a radar transponder on a platform, while TV Tracker uses a TV imaging system for position reference. In general these above-named systems are less accurate and reliable than the three described beforehand, with the exception of Fanbeam, which is still (1993) in the experimental stage.

Heading reference is provided by the gyro compass, which is a standard fitment in all vessels. For redundancy purposes a second or even third gyro may be fitted. An input to the DP must be provided representing the wind direction and strength. This is achieved via a transmitting anemometer or windsensor. This input allows direct compensation, by thrusters, for the wind speed and direction. This is especially important when the wind is gusting or changing rapidly.

The majority of DP-capable vessels have a diesel-electric power system. Power is generated in electrical form on a power station basis and is used to drive all vessel functions. A number of alternators are driven by individual diesel engines, and produce high-voltage alternating current. This power is distributed by means of a high-voltage switchboard to such items as thrusters, fire pump motors and crane

Figure 20: *The Differential Global Positioning System.* (David Bray)

motors. Power is further transformed down to lower voltages for auxiliary and domestic uses on lower-voltage switchboards. Diesel-electric is very versatile, with power generation provided by between four and eight alternators, often located in two separate machinery spaces. Alternators may be started or stopped allowing demand and supply to be matched most economically, with the required amount of reserve power available. The DP electronics are powered through an Uninterruptible Power Supply (UPS), ensuring fully redundant main power supply with a battery back-up to cover blackout situations.

Manoeuvrability is supplied through the vessel's main propellers and rudder, and from a variety of thrusters. The main propeller arrangement may be single or twin screw, fixed or controllable pitch. Twin rudders may or may not form part of the DP system. If not, the rudder is maintained in the amidships position. The main types of thrusters found in DP vessels are azimuth thrusters and tunnel thrusters. Azimuth thrusters can be rotated through a full 360°, so that thrust can be applied with any force in any direction. While ideal for DP, two or three azimuth thrusters located at the stern may also be used for main propulsion, with steering provided by link to the autopilot. Azimuth thrusters may be fixed, or they may be retractable into the hull. Tunnel thrusters are invariably CP (controllable pitch) propellers, placed athwartships in a tunnel at the bow or stern of the vessel. They are used to change or maintain vessel heading, or to control her position in a 'sideways' direction.

Essential to the safe operation of DP vessels are properly trained and qualified key personnel. Master, deck officers (acting as DP operators), electrical and electronics officers and engineers all need to be fully competent. Training for masters and DPOs is available within a scheme administered by the Nautical Institute. Two shore-based courses, available in Lowestoft and Aberdeen, are sandwiched with trainee sea-time aboard DP vessels. The Nautical Institute DP Operators Certificate and Logbook are recognized world-wide. Training for engineering and electrical staff is available from the DP system manufacturers.

When DP first made an appearance as an operating technique, the only vessels to use the capability were coring and drilling vessels. Much deep-water exploration drilling was carried out using DP, and as the equipment developed and became more reliable, the benefits of using DP for other functions became apparent. At the present time DP is used in many different vessel types and operations.

In offshore oilfield locations a large number of tasks need to be done by divers, including sub-sea installation, inspection, cleaning, repair and survey work. Often a platform installation will carry a diving spread but equally often space precludes this. Accordingly a dive support vessel (DSV) may be used. In shallow water areas an air-diving operation may be mounted from a vessel using anchors and mooring lines to the platform

The stern view of an air diving support vessel. This type of vessel does not have dynamic positioning and relies on a four-point anchor system or the deployment of the two bow anchors and mooring to a platform at the stern. The container units house the dive control, decompression chambers and other ancillary equipment. The divers' deployment basket is at the right of the picture and the umbilical rack is behind it. (Oceaneering)

for positioning. Recently this option has dropped out of favour because of the amount of hardware on the seabed which precludes the laying of anchors.

During the last 15 years a large number of DSVs have been built with a DP capability, and their preferred and normal method of operation is to use DP for positioning. These vessels are very versatile, usually having a large amount of deck space, cranage, accommodation for con-

tracting personnel and other facilities. Most have an emergency intervention role and are fitted with fire monitors, helideck and medical facilities. An air diving spread may deploy a basket or wet bell to 50 m (165 ft) depth, while a saturation diving spread may operate one or two bells at depths of up to 500 m (1,640 ft).

A typical DSV is approximately 90 m (295 ft) in length and is diesel-electric powered. One or two diving bells are

Oceaneering's Ocean Diver *is an early example of an air diving support vessel fitted with a crane. To stay on location at the work site, the vessel would deploy anchors. Racks at the bow and stern hold the anchors secure when they are not in use.* (Oceaneering)

The dynamically positioned diving support vessel (DPDSV) Rockwater 2 *in open water. The vessel has a full saturation diving capability and can deploy ROVs or other underwater vehicles. (Rockwater)*

A diving support vessel steams away from a North Sea oil platform and shows the effectiveness of the water cannons which are used in the event of a major fire on a platform. The 'Stena Seaspread' class of vessel incorporates a full 12-man saturation diving complex. (Rockwater)

deployed through a moonpool in the centre of the vessel. The vessel will also be equipped with an ROV. Propulsion and manoeuvring is provided through (typically) six propellers, a common arrangement being three tunnel thrusters forward, with three azimuth thrusters aft. These propellers are all used as part of the DP system for position keeping.

A DSV of this type is not restricted simply to operating divers. She is able to mobilize for complex surface or sub-sea operations that may need the intervention of divers. DSVs typically carry out installation of sub-sea or surface hardware, lay cables and pipes, recover lost or damaged items from the seabed, or carry out survey work.

MRSVs are typically large semi-submersible barges with a DP capability which are able to supply all the installation, maintenance, repair and emergency support necessary for one oilfield. They are very large vessels with similar facilities to those of the DSVs described above but on a more extensive scale. Able to operate in almost any weather conditions, a vessel of this type may be supporting a number of different operations simultaneously. Often their major role is in providing 'flotel' accommodation facilities for personnel engaged in construction operations on an adjacent platform, connected by a gangway or bridge. Invariably with diesel-electric power and propulsion facilities, the DP system will always be fully redundant, as for DSVs, with up to ten thrusters for manoeuvrability.

Wherever offshore oilfields are found, crane barges are required to install the largest platform and topside structures. Most of these barges rely upon anchors for positioning but a few of the largest of them are DP-capable. One such crane barge is the *DB 102* operated by

Construction work requiring heavy lift crane capability, large deck space accommodation facilities, workshops, a stable work vessel and a twin bell saturation diving system are the key elements offered by a semi-submersible. The Rockwater Semi 1 is such a vessel. Below the large crane is the hyperbaric lifeboat, with the diving bell launches either side. They stabilize the bells to well below the water line during launch and recovery. (Rockwater)

Heeremac, which has twin cranes each of 6,000 tonnes capacity and is thus able to lift up to 12,000 tonnes in one lift. Another barge of this type is the *M 7000*, which has twin 7,000 tonne cranes. The configuration of these barges is semi-submersible, and the DP capability allows them to work in a very short weather-window. Even a large topside or jacket structure can be located and installed in 6–12 hours, so a barge can operate in the winter months and make use of calm weather periods to complete lifts. Without DP such an operation could be extended by days due to the need to lay anchors, thus precluding the ability to take advantage of short good weather opportunities.

Survey vessels are used for a variety of functions, ranging from hydrographic survey, seismic survey, pipe or cable pre-lay survey to underwater inspection tasks. Many of these tasks involve the deployment of submersible vehicles, remotely operated (ROVs) and fitted with extensive instrumentation. Survey vessels are often conversions from other vessel types, and the DP system may be a retro-fit. Usually redundancy is not required in these DP systems as the operations tend to be of a less critical nature. The DP system may be configured to enable the vessel to maintain position in the normal way, to follow a pre-determined track or to follow an underwater vehicle automatically.

Deep water drilling operations provided one of the first uses for DP techniques. Early DP drillships were monohull vessels of between 15,000 and 20,000 tonnes displacement. A vessel of this type may alter her heading continually in order to 'weathervane'. This reduces the fuel consumption and enables improved position keeping in adverse weather conditions. Modern drillships are large semi-submersibles of around 60,000 tonnes displacement, able to drill and complete wells in water depths exceeding 2,000 m (6,564 ft). In water as deep as this the main consideration is not absolute geographical position but 'stack/riser angle'.

A drillship is connected to the seabed by a complex riser system. On the seabed is placed the lower riser package, or 'stack', carrying the blowout preventer (BOP). The drillstring runs down the riser, through the stack into the well. The riser carries drilling mud down the hole, and mud plus rock cuttings are carried back up to the surface. In deep water a tidal stream will cause the riser to 'bow', necessitating the vessel moving uptide to avoid damage to the drillstring. What is important is not the position of the ship but the differential angle between the stack and

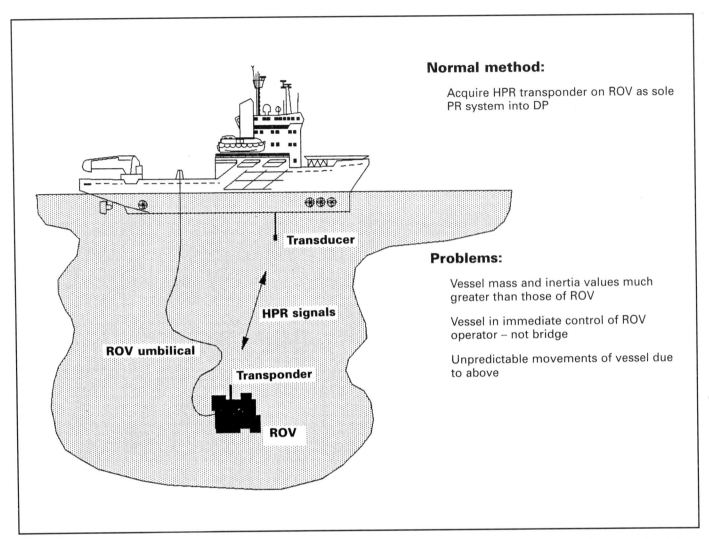

Normal method:

Acquire HPR transponder on ROV as sole
PR system into DP

Transducer

Problems:

Vessel mass and inertia values much
greater than those of ROV

HPR signals

Vessel in immediate control of ROV
operator – not bridge

Unpredictable movements of vessel due
to above

ROV umbilical

Transponder

ROV

Figure 21: *The system
that allows a DP vessel to
follow an ROV.* (David
Bray)

the riser. Inclinometer sensors placed on
stack and riser detect this angle and transmit the information back up the riser to
the DP system. The vessel position is continually adjusted accordingly to reduce
this angle to zero. This facility is known as
'floating set point'. Modern drillships are
able to work in deep water exposed locations and very severe weather conditions.
They are typified by large amounts of
power and redundancy. At locations
remote from land, position reference
becomes a problem. This can be provided
from satellite-based systems, deep water
Taut Wire or specialist HPR.

A number of drillships are also fitted for
thruster assisted mooring. This is a development of DP technology which includes
anchors and mooring lines in the system.
Mooring line lengths, directions and tensions are all monitored by the system. The

vessel will set up on position having laid a
pattern of around eight anchors. Mooring
lines are tensioned and the system applies
thruster power to maintain those tensions
and thus position at calm weather values.
Thus the positioning is mainly achieved by
the mooring lines, while environmental
forces are compensated for by the
thrusters. In addition, an analysis is continually being run on the consequences of
any line break, so that if one or more
mooring lines are lost the vessel can maintain position using added thruster power
without overloading the remaining intact
mooring lines.

Cable ships have special requirements
for manoeuvrability. Station keeping
while carrying out jointing or repair, or
the precise following of a track or underwater vehicle, are all part of the duty of a
cable vessel. Most modern cables are of

the fibre-optic variety which, although they may have operational advantages, are much more fragile in terms of strength. DP allows more precise positioning work and most (if not all) new-building cable vessels are fitted with DP. Many cable lay operations involve the use of a plough. The plough is towed by the vessel, ploughs a trench, lays the cable and buries it in one operation. The DP system is fed with plough hawser tension and direction information so that the vessel can automatically compensate, for example, if the plough strikes harder ground, and increase thruster power to maintain speed.

Specialist vessels are employed in the industry to lay steel pipelines on the seabed. Hitherto these barges were manoeuvred using anchors, and progress was accompanied by anchors continually being lifted and repositioned ahead of the vessel. Pipe is constructed on deck from 12 m (39 ft) sections, the completed pipe being launched down a 'stinger' or ramp at the stern. Increasingly DP is being used instead of anchors for positioning. Two vessels of this type are *Lorelay* and *Solitaire*. In addition to controlling the position of the vessel the DP must also maintain the required value of pipe tension; failure to do this results in the pipe sustaining damage.

A somewhat unorthodox application of DP is in the control of the positioning of tankers engaged in loading crude oil at

offshore loading terminals. Many fields do not have export pipelines to the beach, but export by tanker. The loading terminal may be a buoy, a floating spar, an articulated tower or a rigid tower. The tanker moors to a terminal using a hawser, and loads cargo through a hose and bow manifold. This method becomes hazardous in severe weather, especially in exposed locations, and a lot of downtime results from the tanker having to 'wait on weather' if the terminal has been disconnected because of the weather.

The pipelines which carry oil and gas from the offshore platforms to the onshore processing plant, or to a loading buoy offshore, can measure up to 762 mm (30 in) in diameter. They are made of steel and require protection in the form of a concrete coating. The joining, preparation and laying of pipelines requires specialist vessels like this one, known as 'lay barges'.

Oil recovered from beneath the ocean floor to an oil platform has to be transported ashore. This can be by pipeline or oil tanker. Loading a tanker at sea requires a loading buoy. One type which has seen service in the North Sea and other oil producing countries throughout the world is the Single Buoy Mooring (SBM). Once the tanker is moored to the buoy, a hose connected to it is passed to the tanker to enable oil to be transferred.

The weather and sea state criteria may be extended considerably if DP techniques are used, allowing the tanker to dispense with the hawser. Typically, a tanker may be between 100,000 and 175,000 tonnes deadweight, fitted with main propeller (single or twin screw), a tunnel thruster at the stern and two at the bow. Navigational, DP, mooring and loading control functions are all placed in a forward bridgehouse. The DP system continually calculates a weathervane heading such that the tanker lies head-to-weather a fixed distance from the terminal; as weather conditions alter, the vessel automatically acquires a new heading to remain head-to-weather. Position reference is obtained from HPR, with a ring of transponders placed around the terminal, and Artemis, with a Fixed station placed on the tower.

Many North Sea oilfields are very marginal in terms of output, and the quantity of recoverable oil may not justify the investment required in constructing an array of production platforms, especially in deep water. This is another area where DP may provide a solution. Production facilities can be placed aboard a purpose-built vessel, either a semi-submersible or a monohull, containing storage facilities for recovered oil. Flexible risers connect the vessel to wellheads on the seabed below. When the field becomes depleted, the vessel can be relocated to another field. This floating production vessel may be positioned by mooring to anchors, or by thruster assisted mooring, or by DP alone.

The BP floating production vessel *Seillean* is an example of this type of ves-

Figure 22: *The system used by a DP tanker to hold position on a loading terminal.* (David Bray)

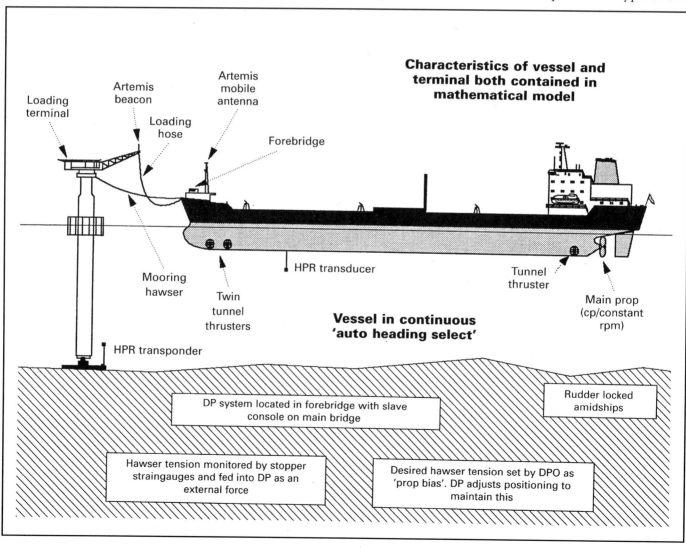

sel. Of monohull construction, positioning is by DP with flexible risers connecting to two wells. When loading is complete, she uncouples from the wellheads and steams to the offload port. She is also able to anchor in a sheltered location and offload to a conventional shuttle tanker moored alongside. A different configuration is found in the *Petrojarl*. This vessel is a turret-moored monohull, wherein a large circular turntable or turret forms the centre body of the vessel's hull. The turret itself is moored to a spread of anchors, while the vessel weathervanes around the turret under the control of the DP system. The vessel stays on location, offloading production to a DP shuttle tanker on location astern.

DP technology is being applied to dredgers, both the type used in the recovery of roadstone and aggregates, and those used for port and channel maintenance. New vessels of this type are often fitted with a non-redundant DP system with automatic track-follow capability. Specialist vessels of a similar type are employed to carry out trenching operations prior to pipelay. These vessels may deploy a tracked seabed crawler vehicle controlled from the surface. A number of small bulk carriers are fitted for this task, enabling them to carry out protection work on a pipeline. The vessels are fitted with automatic self-unloading conveyor belt systems, together with a controllable fall pipe. The DP system enables precision track-following, allowing stone to be placed with accuracy. Smaller vessels still carry deckloads of stone which can be discharged by a tipper arrangement. These vessels are able to position close in to the legs of platform structures so that stone can be placed to prevent erosion around the piles. Again, the precision of DP allows a task to be completed that would otherwise be impossible.

Recently, some commercial vessels such as container ships, ro-ro ferries and heavy lift ships have been fitted with a simple DP system to allow precision manoeuvring at port turnarounds. The newest Finnish icebreakers are DP-capable, giving them the ability to carry out DP functions in oilfield work during the summer months (when they would otherwise be laid up). DP has also been put to good use in the latest series of minehunters built for the Royal Navy.

Chapter 16

The Future

STEVEN SPIELBERG HAS created a vision of the future for undersea exploration and adventure with his TV series *Seaquest DSV*. Roaming the oceans in a super technologically advanced submarine complete with talking dolphin captures the imagination and paints an appealing picture of this alien environment. It is in fact impossible to predict how future undersea exploration by either man, machine or mammals will develop. What for example would have been the reaction of the survivors of the *Titanic* disaster in 1912 had they been told that 73 years later, a small three-man submarine equipped with a small remote operated vehicle would survey the inside of the wreck, and then be able to transmit colour pictures of it around the world, to be seen in the homes of millions of people? For those survivors such a concept would have been beyond anything that they could have imagined, so what will another 70 years bring us?

To have man living and working under the sea has been the dream of scientists for many years, but for the foreseeable future it remains just a dream. There will be projects involving undersea habitats, hotels and tourist attractions, but major projects such as the Pilkington Glass Age Development Sea City plan are not financially viable. This aimed to combine an underwater and above-water complex, all of which would be encompassed within a man-made harbour in order that the complex could be protected against storms and strong underwater currents. The inhabitants could live and work at various levels. There would be access to the seabed where aquanauts could leave the habitat and work at fish farming, the recovery of seabed materials and minerals and the cultivation of undersea plants for export. There would be a variety of undersea vehicles, both seabed tractors and free-swimming, which could undertake survey and mechanical tasks. An undersea complex would need to be self-sufficient and the Sea City was designed to include a desalination plant that could treat seawater to produce fresh water for the city and export the excess. It was also envisaged that heating and electrical power would be provided from gas supplied from a sub-sea gas production wellhead. Such a city may be technically possible, but the immense costs of such a project place it well into the future.

Even deploying divers into the deeper oceans appears to be developing its own problems. Doctors and scientists are undertaking research into the long-term health effects that may occur as a result of deep saturation dives. There are a number of professional Norwegian divers who have failed their diving medical examinations and can no longer dive. If there prove to be long-term health implications which affect the lungs, spine and brain, then that will affect the use of man in conventional diving equipment working in the deep oceans, which will in turn alter the future of undersea work and exploration.

Man's undersea adventures will continue as oil and gas exploration and recovery moves into deeper water and scientists seek more information from the oceans. This means that underwater robots using advanced computer technology and satellite systems will take the lead. The super-intelligent vehicles will be able to roam the oceans, gathering data and carrying out work tasks. Coupled to this will be the continuing research of undersea explorers such as Robert Ballard, and his expeditions to locate and film wrecks such as the *Bismarck* and the *Lusitania* using remote controlled vehicles – work which will allow everybody to be witness to the exploration of the Earth's last frontier, the oceans.

Useful Addresses

General Addresses

Director of the Associates
Woods Hole Oceanographic Institution
Woods Hole
Mass 02543, USA

The Whale Conservation Institute
191 Weston Road
Lincoln
MA 01773, USA

Marine Information and Advisory Service
Institute of Oceanographic Sciences
Deacon Laboratory
Brook Road
Wormley
Godalming
Surrey GU8 5UB

Ocean Drilling Programme
Texas A & M University
1000 Discovery Drive
College Station
TX 77845-9547, USA

The American Cetacean Society
PO Box 2639
San Pedro
CA 90731, USA

Earthwatch
PO Box 403 N
Watertown
MA 02772, USA

The Ocean Society
Building E
Fort Mason Centre
San Francisco
CA 94123, USA

The British Divers Marine Life Rescue
Mill Cottage
Windmill Hill
Brenchley
Kent TN12 7NR

The Historical Diving Society
23 Brompton Drive
Brierley Hill
West Midlands DY5 3NZ

The Historical Diving Society
1223 Wilshire Blvd
Unit 119
Santa Monica
CA 90403, USA

Deep Sea Adventure
9 Custom House Quay
Old Harbour
Weymouth
Dorset DT4 8BG

Sub Aqua Association
5 Bothwell Street
Edinburgh
Scotland

British Sub Aqua Club
Telford's Quay
Ellesmere Port
South Wirral
Cheshire L65 4FY

PADI International
Unit 9
The 306 Estate
Broomhill Road
Brislington
Bristol BS4 5RG

Discover the World
Whale and Dolphin Watching
The Flatt Lodge
Bewcastle
Nr Carlisle
Cumbria CA6 6PH

Whale and Dolphin Conservation Society
19a James Street West
Bath
Avon BA1 2BT

Research and Consultancy
Becketts Cottage
Bungay Road
Hempnall
Norwich NR15 2NG

The Maritime Centre
Lowestoft College
St Peters Street
Lowestoft NR32 2NB

International Association of Underwater
    Engineering Contractors
177a High Street
Beckenham
Kent BR3 1AH

Society for Underwater Technology
76 Mark Lane
London EC3R 7JN

Offshore Research Focus
Techword Services
153–155 London Road
Hemel Hempstead
Herts HP3 9SQ

HSE Approved Professional Diver Training Schools

Fort Bovisand Underwater Centre
Fort Bovisand
Plymouth
Devon PL9 0AB

Prodive Ltd
Falmouth Oil Exploration Base
Falmouth Docks
Cornwall TR11 4NR

The Underwater Centre
Fort William
Inverness-shire PH33 6LZ

Diver Training School (Commercial
    Division)
5 Camperdown Terrace
Exmouth
Devon EX8 1EJ

The Commercial Diving Centre
13 Ravine Road
Canford Cliffs
Poole
Dorset BH13 7HS

Interdive Ltd
West Hoe Road
Plymouth
Devon PL1 3BH

Statens Dykkerskole
Norwegian Government Diver Training
    School
Skaleviksveien 60
Postboks 53
5073 Skalevikneset
Bergen
Norway

Netherland Diving Centre
Schoemakerstraat 97
PO Box 6067
2600 Ja Delft
Holland

Institut National De Plongée
    Professionnelle
Entrée No. 3
Port de la Pointe Rouge
13008 Marseille
France

USA Professional Diver Training Schools

College of Oceaneering
272 South Fries Road
Wilmington
CA 90744

The Ocean Corporation
10840 Rockley Road
PO Box 721738
Houston
TX 77272-1738

Divers Institute of Technology Inc.
4315 11th Avenue N.W.
PO Box 70667
Seattle
WA 98107-0667

Divers Academy of the Eastern Seaboard
2500 South Broadway
Camden
NJ 08104

Santa Barbara City College Marine
    Technology Programme
721 Cliff Drive
Santa Barbara
CA 93109

International Commercial Diving Institute
550 South Madison Street
Wilmington
DE 19801

Bibliography

U.S. Navy Diving Manual (Best Publishing Co, USA)

Reg Vallintine, *Divers and Diving* (Blandford Press)

Robert H. Davis, *Deep Diving and Submarine Operations* (Siebe Gorman & Co. Ltd)

Dr T. F. Gaskell (ed.), *Using the Oceans* (The Queen Anne Press Ltd)

The Professional Diver's Handbook (Submex Ltd)

R. Frank Busby, *Manned Submersibles* (Office of the Oceanographer of the Navy, United States Navy)

Jane's Ocean Technology, *Jane's Yearbooks* (Jane's Publishing Company)

Forest G. Wood, *Marine Mammals and Man: The Navy's Porpoises and Sealions* (Robert B. Luce Inc., USA)

Alain Dunoyer de Seronzac, *Un Conquérant Sous La Mer* (Buchet Chastel, France)

Jackie Warner and Fred Park, *Requiem for a Diver* (Brown, Son & Ferguson)

Dr Robert D. Ballard, *The Discovery of the Titanic* (Guild Publishing, London)

Dr Robert D. Ballard, *The Discovery of the Bismarck* (Hodder & Stoughton/Madison Press)

Dr Robert D. Ballard, *Exploring the Bismarck* (Hodder & Stoughton/Madison Press)

Barrie Penrose, *Stalin's Gold* (Granada Publishing, London)

Index